GALAXIES AND THE UNIVERSE

Galaxies

VETLESEN PRIZE RECIPIENTS

and the Universe

LODEWIJK WOLTJER

Editor

THE VETLESEN SYMPOSIUM

HELD AT COLUMBIA UNIVERSITY

ON OCTOBER 19, 1966

COLUMBIA UNIVERSITY PRESS

1968 *New York and London*

PREFACE

THE VETLESEN PRIZE was established at Columbia University by the G. Unger Vetlesen Foundation in 1959 for outstanding achievement in the sciences, resulting in a clearer understanding of the earth, its history, and its relation to the universe.

On the occasion of the 1966 Vetlesen Prize award to Jan Hendrik Oort, Professor of Astronomy at the University of Leiden and Director of the Leiden University Observatory, a one-day symposium was held at Columbia University following the award ceremony on October 18. The 1966 Vetlesen lecture given by Professor Oort, the other invited lectures given at this symposium, as well as an appreciation of the prize recipient given by Professor Bengt Strömgren at the award ceremony, are included in this symposium volume.

L. Woltjer, Editor

INVITED LECTURERS

BENGT STRÖMGREN, at the time of the 1966 Vetlesen Award, Professor at the Institute for Advanced Study, Princeton. Currently Professor of Astronomy at Copenhagen University.

JAN H. OORT, Professor of Astronomy and Director of the Observatory, University of Leiden.

C. C. LIN, Institute Professor and Professor of Applied Mathematics, Massachusetts Institute of Technology.

BRUNO ROSSI, Institute Professor and Professor of Physics, Massachusetts Institute of Technology.

ALLAN SANDAGE, Staff Member, Mount Wilson and Palomar Observatories.

BENGT
STRÖMGREN / An Appreciation
/ of Jan Hendrik Oort

IT IS A GREAT PRIVILEGE to have the opportunity to address you
on this happy occasion. This is the first time that the Vetlesen
Prize has gone to an astronomer, and it is a particular privilege
for me today to speak of Jan Oort and his work. The Vetlesen
Prize is awarded for outstanding achievement in the sciences,
resulting in a clearer understanding of the earth, its history, and
its relation to the universe. If today we have a clearer understanding of the history of the earth and its relation to the universe
than we had three of four decades ago we owe this partly to
astronomers who through their research work have provided some
of the foundations for the investigations in question. Detailed
knowledge of the structure, kinematics, and dynamics of our
Galaxy pertaining to stellar as well as interstellar components has
been obtained. Insight has also been given into the nature of the
forces of evolution at work in every part of the Galaxy. Among
the astronomers who have contributed to this knowledge,
Professor Oort in the opinion of the astronomical community
ranks highest.

Professor Oort made an outstanding contribution when he
showed in 1927, through an analysis of the radial velocities of
relatively distant high-luminosity stars, that our Galaxy rotates
around an axis at right angles to the plane of the milky way. This
takes us back to a period in the development of astronomy that

to us in our work today is of crucial importance. A countryman of Jan Oort, Kapteyn, devoted a lifetime to the study of the structure of our Galaxy. Many of his results are valid today. But, as has happened many times in the development of our science, in some respects the picture has changed very significantly. The change of view took place in the 1920s. Shapley discovered that outside what we now call the local system of stars there was a population of objects clustering around a center at great distance from our local system. To begin with, the meaning of this was not clearly understood. But the first hint of the direction in which the new picture would be developed came through an investigation by Professor Oort of the high-velocity stars. High-velocity stars had been studied, their proper motions had been determined, and a little was known about this peculiar kind of star that seemed to move through our region of space with much higher velocities than the typical star. To begin with, many of those who were worrying about such problems as the determination of the motion of the sun relative to the stars regarded these objects, the high-velocity stars, as nuisances. The first systematic study is due to Professor Oort, and it pointed the way toward the ultimate solution. Jan Oort's investigations were followed by pioneering work of Bertil Lindblad, who formulated the hypothesis that our local system is but a small part of a huge galaxy centered around the region indicated by the globular clusters and rotating with the high speed of about 300 kilometers per second around an axis at right angles to its largest dimension. But it was only through Professor Oort's detailed analysis of the observational material then available that the hypothesis was finally proved. This is an example of one paper changing the whole outlook of the astronomical community. The conclusion drawn by Professor Oort at the time was final; it was accepted, and from then on this was the frame of reference in which all discussions of the dynamics and kinematics in our system of stars were carried out.

In the 1930s Professor Oort returned to an analysis of the type that Kapteyn had carried out. He tried to evaluate more in detail the spatial distribution of the stars in the Galactic System, with emphasis on the nearest several thousand light years. The new element in the analysis was the fact that it had become quite clear that our Galaxy is full of absorbant matter, and that this was the reason why Kapteyn was led to the conclusion that we are in an island, the local system. The absorption is due to small particles, interstellar matter that occupies the space between the stars near the main plane of the Galaxy. This interstellar dust obscures the view; we cannot see very distant stars in the plane of the Galaxy. And this absorption must be taken into account in all studies of galactic structure.

In these studies, also, Professor Oort's answers were final, as far as analysis on the basis of the observational material in question goes. I would like at this point to quote words that I think describe Oort's contribution very well, words by the President of the Royal Astronomical Society, Professor Harry Plaskett, spoken in 1946 on the occasion of the award to Professor Oort of the gold medal of the Royal Astronomical Society. Professor Plaskett said then: "In spite of the clouds of smoke, both literal and metaphorical, which obscure its form, the Galactic System seems at length to have met its master in the thoroughness of our Medalist, working quietly and thoughtfully in his room at Leiden." This was, and is, to all of us a most remarkable achievement, but in a way it was only a beginning, for during the following decades a whole new branch of astronomy developed, radio astronomy. This development was brought about by the work of a number of research groups that emerged after World War II, and one of the most important ones was the Leiden group under the leadership of Professor Oort. His collaborator, van de Hulst, had made the prediction that interstellar matter, which consists mostly of hydrogen, would be visible in radio-astronomical observations in the form of an emission line at the wavelength of 21 centimeters. In the early 1950s this prediction, made independently by van de Hulst and Shklovskii, was verified; and this led to a new era in the exploration of our Galaxy. At the same time other forms of radio emission from interstellar matter in the Galaxy were further explored, and the results proved to be very valuable in galactic research. The following years brought extremely important progress, in part because astronomers now possessed a tool that was no longer hindered by the clouds of dust to which Professor Plaskett had referred. The 21-centimeter radiation goes right through the Galaxy, and the Galaxy can be explored to its farthest corners.

Professor Oort as one of the leaders in this enterprise took a very active part in the exploration, and on this occasion I wish to emphasize the importance of some of the findings that are due to Professor Oort and his close collaborators. In the early work on the rotation of the Galaxy, it had been possible to find to a fair approximation, within one or two degrees, the direction to the center of our Galaxy. Professor Oort, in collaboration with his colleagues at the Leiden Observatory, through radio-astronomical work achieved a determination, the uncertainty of which was minutes of arc instead of degrees. It is indeed most remarkable that in the lifetime of one astronomer, and through his efforts, this should have been accomplished. But more than that, the whole structure of the central region of the Galaxy was explored, and very important new phenomena were discovered. We now see how matter is streaming out of the central parts, and evidently a very important feature in the structure of the Galaxy has been added to our picture.

During the last few years a problem of enormous importance has occupied Professor Oort and his collaborators in Leiden as well as other groups of radio astronomers. It has become clear through analysis of 21-centimeter observations that we are being bombarded from space outside our Galaxy by high-velocity clouds, and we are now in a very exciting period when every year new observations of this important phenomenon are added. It is already clear that we are confronted with a phenomenon that plays an enormous role in the whole household of our Galactic System.

I have mentioned a number of outstanding contributions by Professor Oort. This is by no means all that he has achieved. It would be a pleasure and a privilege to continue, but this would lead us too far. I would, however, like to say a few words about one of Professor Oort's investigations in another field. The exploration of the Galaxy has given us the framework to which we refer in every discussion of the evolution of the solar system and the earth, and the results that Professor Oort achieved are of fundamental importance to all who work on the problems of the history of the earth. However, Professor Oort has concerned himself also with the solar system itself. He has made a very important contribution to our knowledge of comets. When he started this work, it had been known for quite some time that a large fraction of the comets come from regions far beyond the system of the planets. And now Professor Oort has shown that they come from a fairly narrow range of distances, and that as they pass through the solar system this narrowness in the distribution of aphelium distances is destroyed. The perturbations of the planets, as was expected from previous work, blot it out. This led Professor Oort to the conclusion that among the comets that come in from the outer regions of the solar system a large fraction, if not all, must be new, that is, they come into the inner part of the solar system for the first time. The consequence was a new understanding regarding the distribution of matter in the solar system. We must assume the presence of a reservoir of matter far out, much farther out than the outermost planets; a reservoir, out of which comets occasionally are deflected into the inner regions of the solar system, where they become visible to observers on the earth.

Professor Oort's outstanding contributions made it clear to those who made the choice for the Vetlesen Prize that he should be the first astronomer to receive the Prize. On this occasion I would like to mention a few other features of the whole picture that we are so happy about this evening. Professor Oort not only has contributed through his own researches, but he has been outstanding as a leader in his field. His contributions to the international organization, the International Astronomical Union, are well known. I think I do not exaggerate when I say that Professor Oort, as General Secretary and as President of the Union, has contributed more than anyone else to transforming it into a Union in which research and collaboration in research come first. But his influence in contemporary astronomy goes much further than that. Whenever there is an important astronomical gathering, Professor Oort's advice is likely to be sought; and I think that through his influence, directly on his students and collaborators and indirectly on a large number of astronomers, he has made a contribution that is also outstanding.

CONTENTS

JAN H. OORT

Radio Astronomical Studies of the Galactic System

THE LARGE-SCALE DISTRIBUTION and the motion of the interstellar gas in a spiral galaxy are the problems that I consider in this paper. To a certain extent these problems can be approached by studying the structure of outside galaxies, such as M 81 or M 51; this approach will doubtlessly become enormously important in the near future. For the present, however, the observations of extragalactic systems are rather restricted, in particular as regards motions. It is therefore important to study our own Galaxy, which is so much closer.

Part of the stars and most of the interstellar gas are concentrated in a relatively thin disk. The thickness of the disk of gas is about one-hundredth of its extent in the galactic plane. The Galaxy also contains another type of population, of nearly spherically symmetrical distribution. This is the so-called halo Population II. It is strongly concentrated toward the center. There are also types of stars which show a distribution intermediate between these two extremes. And, finally, there is the galactic nucleus itself, where, in a relatively small volume, quite unexpected phenomena appear to be produced.

In spiral galaxies the disk is generally the most striking part, though we often also see a central bulge and a nucleus. The halo

1

is usually invisible in outside galaxies, but it is certainly there, as we know from observations in our own Galaxy.

The halo contains stars as well as gas. The gas is difficult to study; the halo of stars can, however, be observed fairly well.

The study of the halo is of extreme importance in connection with the early history of the Galaxy. The halo stars seem now to have arranged themselves in a rather thoroughly mixed, and apparently stationary, state, but in the disk and nucleus this is far from true. Here the evolution is still in full swing, not only in the formation of stars but also with respect to the large-scale structure. We have only to look at a picture of any nearby spiral to see that this is so (see Plate 1).

On such pictures, the nucleus is usually overexposed, and not clearly visible. But in most galaxies real nuclei, i.e., nuclei of small dimension, exist, and in many galaxies these are scenes of surprising activity.

The striking phenomena in disk and nucleus appear to be largely due to the interstellar gas and may therefore be said to be related to the fact that there is still a large quantity of gas that has not been condensed into stars. In the long run this gas will be used up, and probably the structures of all galaxies will then become rather monotonous.

We might say, then, that a spiral or irregular galaxy still bears the stamp of its birth. When we look at pictures like that of M 51, we get at first sight the impression that its structure must be of recent and ephemeral nature. Dr. Lin believes that this is incorrect, and that we are dealing with a lasting, or possibly recurrent, phenomenon kept alive in a rather complicated manner. And we probably must agree with him, mainly on the ground that the lifetimes which would follow from the simplest interpretation of the observed structures and their rotations are much too short.

One of the most interesting indications of the essential role of interstellar gas for the phenomenon of spiral structure is that

PLATE 1. NGC 5194 Spiral nebulae in *Canes Venatici* Messier 51. Satellite nebulae in NGC 5195. 200-inch photograph. (Courtesy of the Mount Wilson and Palomar Observatories.)

virtually no spirals exist in the dense clusters of galaxies. There are plenty of very flat systems in these clusters, so that the necessary conditions for the formation of disk populations have certainly existed, but none of the flat systems show indications of spiral structures or of appreciable content of gas and dust. It was Baade who first saw the importance of this property of cluster galaxies. Spitzer and Baade later suggested that the gas originally present in these galaxies had been swept away by collisions between galaxies, and that after losing their interstellar gas the galaxies had also lost their capacity for making spiral structures. In dense clusters collisions appear to be sufficiently general for most galaxies to have lost their gas.

By investigating the distribution and motion of the interstellar gas we may hope to penetrate best into the mechanism of spiral structure. A formerly undreamt-of possibility to do this was given by the discovery, in 1951, of the 21-cm emission of neutral hydrogen. It is not only the circumstance that this gives us direct information on the gas that makes the 21-cm line observations so important, but especially the fact that the 21-cm radiation penetrates through the dust clouds which at optical wavelengths hide more than 95 per cent of the disk from our view.

The 21-cm radiation gave us for the first time a view on the entire disk of our Galaxy. Though the study of young stellar clusters, which are directly connected with the gas and the spiral structure, can provide extremely valuable information on a region of some 3-kpc radius around the Sun (about one-fifth of the radius of the whole System), a region of this size is quite insufficient for a proper study of the spiral phenomenon, especially because all spiral structure is extremely irregular.

For determining the distribution of the hydrogen in space, as shown in Figure 1, we make use of the differential rotation of the Galaxy. If we knew the rotation curve, and if all the emitting atoms moved with circular velocity around the galactic center, it would be a simple matter to determine their distribution. But the atoms have thermal motions and partake in the random motions in the interstellar medium. To a certain extent we can correct statistically for the effect of these random motions.

But there are also systematic deviations from circular velocity extending over large regions, the effect of which cannot be easily

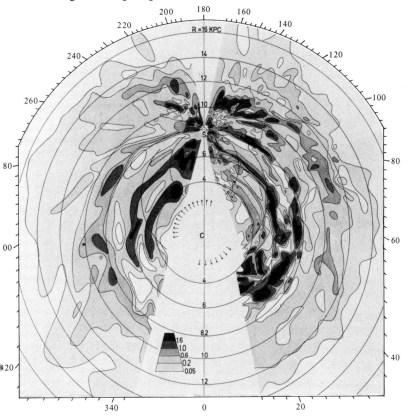

FIGURE 1. Distribution of neutral hydrogen in the galactic plane as determined from observations in the Netherlands (Schmidt, 1957; Westerhout, 1957), and in Australia (Kerr, 1962).

eliminated. The existence of such deviations is most clearly shown if we try to determine the rotation curve from the maximum velocities observed in various longitudes. The rotation curve so derived shows a number of waves which must be due to systematic streamings of gas (Figure 2). These are probably related to the spiral structure. The "waves" exist on both sides of the center.

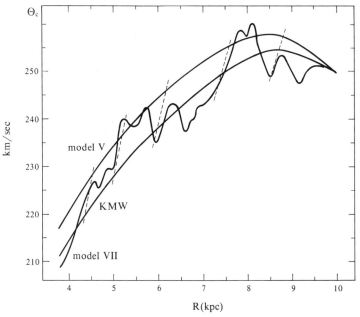

FIGURE 2. Galactic rotation at distances between 4 and 10 kpc from the center derived from 21-cm line profiles (Shane and Smith, 1965).

According to Burton (unpublished) they may be the cause of the apparent asymmetry found by Kerr (1964) between the rotation curves for the Northern and Southern hemispheres. Although the semi-amplitude of the waves (about 10 km per sec) is only a small fraction of the total rotational velocity, the waves add considerably to the difficulty of determining the spiral structure of the interstellar gas from 21-cm observations. At the same time the study of these systematic streamings is of great importance in connection with the dynamics of the spiral structure. An extensive analysis of a large section of the part of the Galaxy inside the Sun's distance from the center is being carried out in Leiden by W. W. Shane and by W. B. Burton. Figure 3 shows preliminary

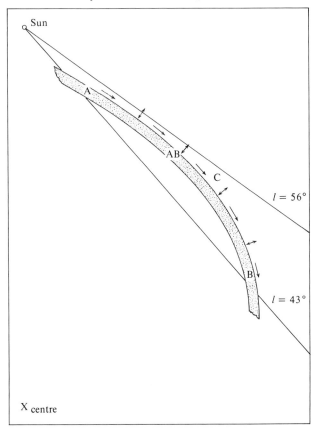

FIGURE 3. Systematic streaming of gas outside the Sagittarius arm (Burton, 1965).

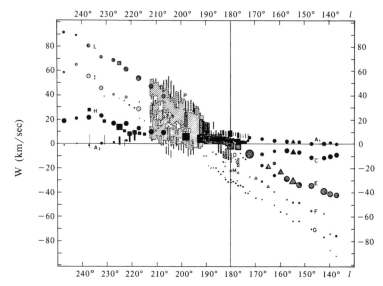

FIGURE 4. Velocities of "arms" in the quadrant around the anticenter (P. O. Lindblad, 1967).

results of Burton's analysis of the so-called Sagittarius arm and its surroundings (Burton, 1965). It appears that the velocity of the gas just outside the arm is higher than the rotation velocity of the arm.

While the deviations from circular motion that we have so far considered are relatively small, much larger deviations exist in the

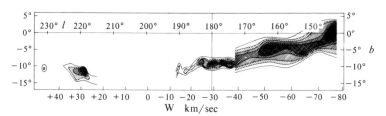

FIGURE 5. Deviation from the galactic plane of a distant arm around the anticenter (P. O. Lindblad, 1967).

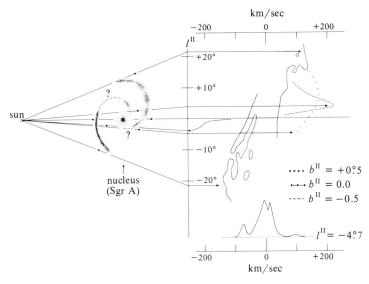

FIGURE 6. Sketch of possible configuration and motion of hydrogen in the central region (Rougoor, 1964).

far outer arms of the System. A striking example was found by Per Olof Lindblad (1967) in an investigation of the anticentral region. Here we find an arm with an inward radial motion of 30 km per sec (Figure 4). At the same time the arm deviates greatly from the galactic plane (Figure 5). Its abnormal motion and position may possibly have been caused by the attraction of the Magellanic Clouds.

It was rather surprising to find that also in the innermost part of the Galaxy large deviations occur, even very much larger than in the outer regions. Within a few kiloparsecs from the center a dense spiral arm is observed which, at the point where it crosses in front of the center, has a radial motion of 53 km per sec toward us. On the far side of the center we observe gas having still higher velocities away from the nucleus, up to perhaps 200 km per sec (Figure 6).

Jan H. Oort

When we come still closer to the nucleus the phenomena seem suddenly to become quite different again. Within 800 pc from the center we see the hydrogen rotating at quite high velocity; at 100 pc from the center the time of revolution is about 3 million years, that is, almost one hundred times faster than in our vicinity (Figure 7). Within this "rotating" region there is a rapid variation

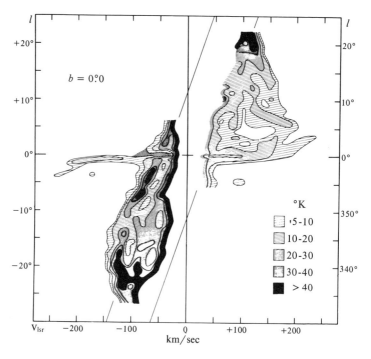

FIGURE 7. Velocity distribution of hydrogen between $-27°$ and $+25°$ galactic longitude, from observations at Dwingeloo (Netherlands) and at the Department of Terrestrial Magnetism (Washington, D.C.). The narrow "wing" of high negative velocities near the center is ascribed to a rapidly rotating "nuclear disk" (Rougoor and Oort, 1960; Rougoor, 1964).

of angular velocity with distance from the center, so that we would expect irregular structures to be rapidly wiped out. Any structures observed in this "nuclear disk" are probably younger than a few million years.

In the central—and probably densest—part of this disk, about 200 pc from the center, we find a concentration of fairly strong radio sources. They stand out particularly well at centimeter waves, where a high resolution can be obtained (Figure 8). Most of the sources are apparently thermal. Mezger and Höglund succeeded in measuring hydrogen recombination lines in two of them. The interpretation of the velocities they found is, however, still uncertain.

However, the most striking radio source in this region is a nonthermal one. As far as we can judge it lies precisely in the direction where the center of mass of our Galaxy is thought to be, and is probably connected with this. The source is small and strongly concentrated towards its center. The radius to half intensity is about 5 pc. Its intrinsic brightness is of the same order as that of Cassiopeia A, and three to five times that of the Crab Nebula. Around the whole complex of condensed sources there is a flattened area of enhanced radiation extending to about 150 pc from the center along the galactic plane (half-intensity radius) and to 50 pc in the perpendicular direction. This radiation is probably synchrotron radiation, like that of the concentrated central source.

Against the central part of the disk quite strong absorption lines of OH have been observed. They show, first, that there must be a large abundance of molecules in the nuclear disk, presumably also of molecular hydrogen, and, second, that there are complex streamings in this disk. For instance, over a range extending to nearly 1° on either side of the center, motions of about 100 km per sec away from the center are observed (Figure 9). In the immediate vicinity of the central source we see an inward current toward this

Jan H. Oort

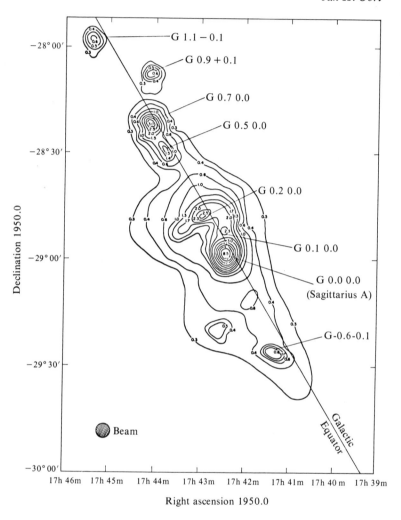

FIGURE 8. Distribution of 3.75-cm radiation from the nuclear region of the Galaxy. Various concentrations are indicated by the letter G followed by numbers giving the galactic longitude and latitude; beamwidth 4'.2 (Downes, Maxwell, and Meeks, 1965).

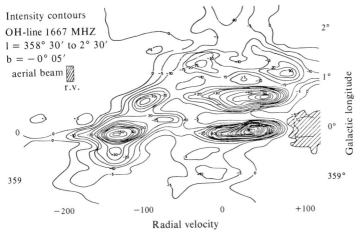

FIGURE 9. OH-absorption in the nuclear region. The strength of the absorption is indicated by negative numbers (Robinson and McGee, 1967).

source, with a velocity of about 60 km per sec. These complicated phenomena have not yet been sufficiently unraveled to present a comprehensible model.

We must now ask how the large expanding features found outside the nuclear disk are to be explained. Let us sum up the facts: Between about 1 kpc and 2 or 3 kpc from the center, the hydrogen shows large systematic radial components in its motion. The motions are directed outward, and vary from about 200 km per sec to 50 km per sec, probably decreasing with increasing distance from the edge of the "nuclear disk." The bulk of this expanding gas is strongly concentrated towards the galactic plane, the thickness between half-density planes being about 250 pc. The total mass of gas involved in this rapid expansion is of the order of 4×10^7 solar masses. Unless there is some way to replenishment, the whole central region up to 2 or 3 kpc would be emptied by this expansion in 30 to 50 million years.

We may ask whether the expansion is perhaps a general feature of the Galaxy. Braes and Shane in Leiden have made various efforts to investigate this question, all with negative results. Similarly, Kerr, in Australia, found no signs of any expansion of the bulk of gas in the Galaxy. The expansion seems to be confined to the central part. It might be caused by: the action of asymmetrical gravitational fields in the Galactic System, pressure of magnetic fields, or an eruptive activity near the nucleus.

It is difficult to judge whether the phenomena might be caused by an asymmetry in the galactic gravitational field or by a large-scale pulsating motion of the gas in the Galaxy. It seems doubtful that the very large outward motions close to the center could be maintained in such a way. Similarly, estimates made by Woltjer and others have indicated that it is unlikely that magnetic fields could be of sufficient strength to cause the observed motions. At the moment the least unlikely explanation would seem to be an explosive activity in the nucleus. But we certainly need more decisive arguments against the other alternatives before we can hold with confidence the supposition of eruptive events on such an enormous scale.

Meanwhile it is extremely interesting to note that recent observations near the nucleus have shown that there is high-velocity gas, with velocities up to about 150 km per sec, apparently moving away from the center under a large angle with the galactic plane. Velocities up to about +120 km per sec are found at longitudes between 0° and −4° and latitudes between +1° and +3°, whereas velocities of −120 km per sec are found in the opposite quadrant, between 0° and +4° longitude and −1° to −3° latitude. In both quadrants the velocities are in a direction opposite to the rotational velocity of the Galaxy and may represent eruptive motions in two diametrically opposite directions. The total mass involved in these motions may be of the order of a million solar masses. These motions were first found by W. W. Shane (Oort, 1968).

A second remarkable phenomenon which is possibly related was recently discovered by Kerr and Sinclair (1966). It concerns the fine structure of the continuous radiation near the center. (See Figure 10.) Besides the main structure in the galactic equator, which we have already mentioned, there is a secondary ridge of

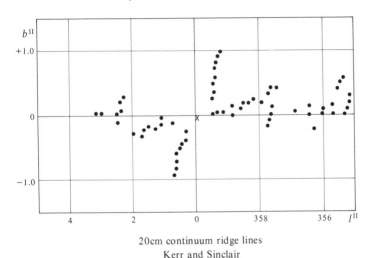

20cm continuum ridge lines
Kerr and Sinclair

FIGURE 10. "Ridges" of continuous radiation at 20 cm near the galactic center (Kerr and Sinclair, 1966).

emission steeply inclined to the galactic circle. This ridge, which can be followed for about 200 pc, lies in the same quadrants as the high-velocity gas. A remarkable property is the very pronounced symmetry with respect to the galactic center. The data are, however, still too fragmentary for speculations concerning the nature of the relation with the high-velocity gas. Two other features occur in the same quadrants, but I will not describe them here.

If eruptive activity is the basis of the expansion phenomena, the eruptions must have swept away the nuclear disk. We can therefore maintain this hypothesis only if we assume that part of

June 1966

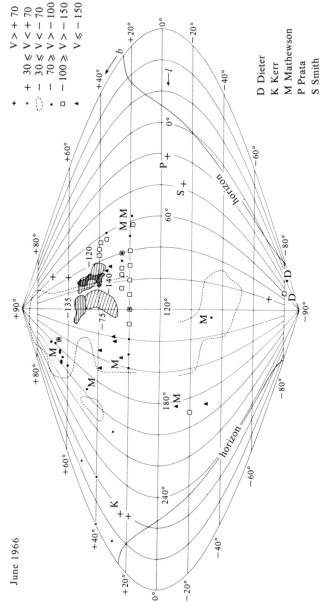

+   V > + 70
×   + 30 ≤ V < + 70
–   – 30 ≤ V < – 70
●   – 70 ≥ V > – 100
□   – 100 ≥ V > – 150
▲   V ≤ – 150

D Dieter
K Kerr
M Mathewson
P Prata
S Smith

FIGURE 11. Distribution of high-velocity gas outside the galactic plane. In the shaded areas gas with an average velocity as indicated in the accompanying numbers is present over practically the whole region. The dashed contours enclose the regions where velocity concentrations between −30 and −70 km per sec have been found by Groningen astronomers. Most of the points at +20° and +25° latitude refer probably to a different phenomenon (namely, a distant arm far above the galactic plane).

the erupted gas has fallen back to the nuclear region, and that on its way it has picked up some angular momentum from the pre-existing disk material. It would then naturally collect into a small fast rotating disk. For material ejected with velocities less than about 500 km per sec this falling back could be completed in roughly ten million years. We would thus have to suppose that the main explosive activity in the nucleus stopped some ten million years ago. Before that it must have continued over a long period, probably several times ten million years. Otherwise we cannot explain why we simultaneously observe very high-velocity gas near the center and much slower outward motions at distances of 2 or 3 kpc.

How such eruptive activity can arise is still an enigma. But, as Ambartsumian has repeatedly pointed out, the nuclei of galaxies give frequent evidence of being the seats of quite unexpected phenomena. Signs of large gas motions near the nuclei have been observed in some nearby galaxies, and actual eruptive phenomena have also been witnessed in several cases. Finally, there is the evidence from radio galaxies and quasars, where everything points to the nuclei as the ultimate, and again eruptive, sources of all the remarkable phenomena observed.

I leave these speculations to discuss a different feature of the Galaxy which has recently become of great interest. Again this feature is concerned with hydrogen moving at high velocity, but now in the outer part of the System. Again the observations were made with the aid of the 21-cm line of hydrogen.

The phenomena were discovered during searches for clouds in high and moderate galactic latitudes made at Harvard, Groningen, and Leiden. Figure 11 shows results for high velocities. We have arbitrarily drawn a limit at 70 km per sec for these high velocities. Velocities between 30 and 70 km per sec will be referred to as intermediate; those below 30 km per sec will be called low velocities. In order not to get confused with ordinary galactic gas, I shall confine myself mainly to observations above 15° latitude.

Figure 12 gives some sample line profiles showing high-velocity "clouds." The distribution of the gas with velocities between −30 and −80 km per sec is shown in Figure 13.

Several things are evident from these observations.

1. All velocities higher than 100 km per sec are negative, i.e., directed toward us. Between ±30 and ±100 km per sec the negative-velocity gas far outweighs gas with positive velocity.

2. The high negative velocities (−70 to −200 km per sec) are almost entirely concentrated in the region of 60° to 200° galactic longitude and +10° to +80° latitude. Apart from the gas at +15° and +20° latitude, which displays different properties, and probably belongs to a far outer part of the galactic disk that has been bent away to a great distance from the galactic plane, there is no indication of any increase in density toward the galactic equator. The center of the region from which the bulk of the high velocities appears to come is situated around $l = 120°$, $b = +40°$.

3. The clouds with intermediate negative velocities generally appear to be concentrated in about the same region, though there may be differences in detail. The intermediate-velocity gas has much greater intensity than the high-velocity gas.

4. Gas of high as well as intermediate velocity is also found in the Southern galactic hemisphere, but in much smaller amount. Again, negative velocities are much more frequent than positive ones. In a very general way the distribution in longitude and latitude for the intermediate velocity clouds can be said to resemble that in the Northern galactic hemisphere. The high velocities are too few to judge; but they display in any case the same characteristic of occurring up to very high latitudes.

5. The high-velocity matter has a pronounced cloudy structure. The velocity dispersion within each cloud is high, averaging about ±10 km per sec.

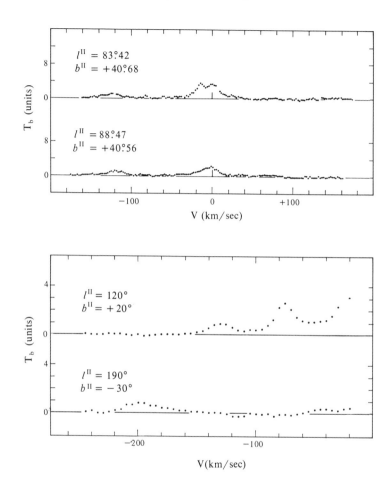

FIGURE 12. Line profiles showing high-velocity hydrogen. *Above:* observations with a bandwidth of 4.2 km per sec (20 kc per sec) and an 8-channel receiver. *Below:* observations with a bandwidth of 10.5 km per sec (50 kc per sec) and a new 20-channel receiver. The scale in the lower half is twice that in the upper profiles (Hulsbosch and Raimond, 1966).

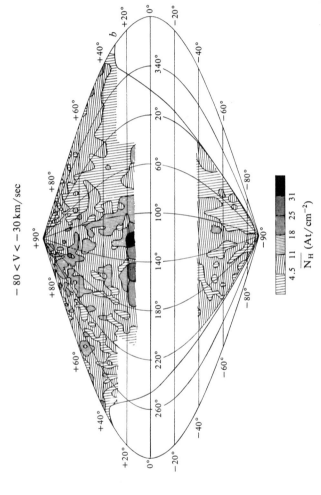

$-80 < V < -30 \text{ km/sec}$

$\overline{N}_H \text{ (At/cm}^{-2}\text{)}$

4.5 11 18 25 31

FIGURE 13. Distribution of hydrogen with velocities between -30 and -80 km per sec in intermediate and high galactic latitudes. The heavier curve shows the declination circle down to which the observations were extended (Blaauw et al., 1967).

We are witnessing what appears to be a rain of gas into the galactic layer, a rain which comes from both sides, though with less intensity from the south.

Where do these clouds come from, and what is the amount of matter they carry into the galactic layer per unit of time? In trying to answer these questions we have first the problem of locating the clouds in space. In the galactic disk we have used the rotation of the Galaxy for determining distances. In the present case, where the velocities deviate widely from the rotation, there is no such possibility. They may be nearby wisps of supernova shells, they may lie far out in the galactic halo, or they may even be outside the Galactic System. The slight information we have on their distances is from optical observations, made by Münch and Zirin (1961), of interstellar absorption lines in some O and B stars far from the plane. They found four clouds with velocities between −30 and −60 km per sec and inferred from their observations that they are probably situated one half to one kpc from the galactic plane. Their clouds are presumably members of our intermediate-velocity group. Though this is admittedly a very weak basis, we shall take it as tentatively indicating that our clouds are situated somewhere in the halo.

The cloudy structure of the high-velocity gas seems to be a fairly general feature. All the high velocities shown were found as isolated humps in the line profiles, indicating that the gas is concentrated in a relatively small velocity interval. It comes, apparently, in distinct clouds. This conclusion is corroborated by the distribution over the sky. For example, the distribution of the hydrogen with a velocity of −175 km per sec around 153° longitude and +38° latitude evidently forms a cloud with a strong central concentration. Like all clouds we see in nature, it has an irregular shape, which is clearly shown in Figure 14, due to Hulsbosch and Raimond and still more strikingly in observations of the same object made by Rougoor at Green Bank (Figure 15).

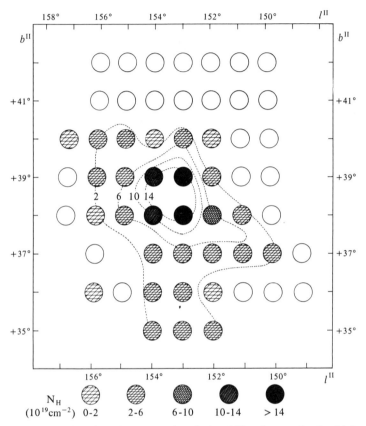

FIGURE 14. "Object A," example of cloud-like feature in the high-velocity gas. Distribution of hydrogen with velocities around -175 km per sec in the region between $148°$ and $158°$ longitude, and $+34°$ and $+43°$ latitude (Hulsbosch and Raimond, 1966).

In some parts the velocity profile appears to be double-peaked. This is the densest high-velocity cloud known. It has an equivalent radius of $1°.8$, or 30 pc if it lies at a distance of 1 kpc. In that case its HI mass is 2500 times that of the Sun, and the velocity of escape from the surface is 1 km per sec. The velocity dispersion is ±12 km per sec in the radial component. With such a dispersion the cloud can have existed only a short time in its present condition. It must expand at a rate of about 10 pc per million years, and during its life it cannot have moved much more than 1 kpc.

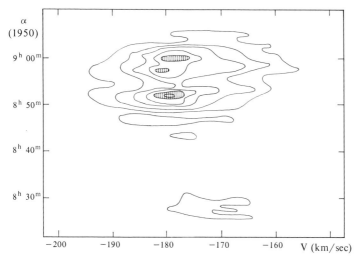

FIGURE 15. Density and velocity distribution in "object A" along the parallel at declination +62°20′. (From observations with the 300-foot telescope in Green Bank; Rougoor, unpublished.)

This conclusion puts a severe limitation on the theories of origin. The cloud I have described is by no means unique. There are several quite small clouds among the highest velocities. There are also features which look different: clouds which cover regions of 10 to 20° on the sky, but nevertheless show the same average velocity over their entire surface (Figures 16 and 17). It may be that these structures are things of the same nature as the condensed clouds, only in a later stage.

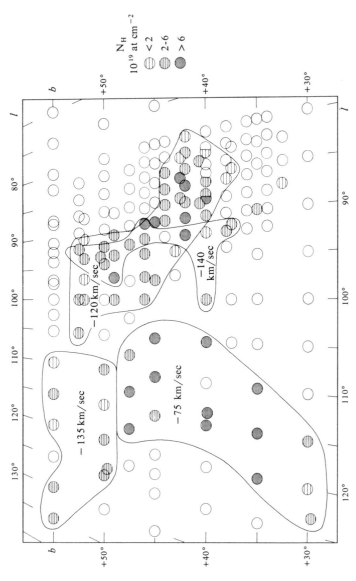

FIGURE 16. Cloud complexes between 80° and 130° galactic longitude. From unpublished observations by Hulshosch (see Oort 1967)

N_H
10^{19} at cm^{-2}
< 2
2 - 6
> 6

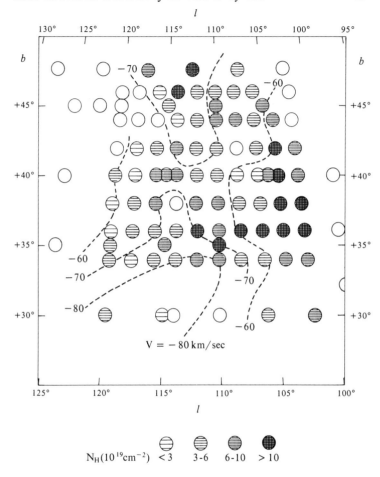

FIGURE 17. Density- and velocity-distribution in the "cloud" with velocity −70 km per sec. From unpublished observations by Hulsbosch (see Oort, 1967).

In the intermediate velocity range the cloudy structure appears in general to become less pronounced; it looks as if the clouds are gradually dissolved as their velocities decrease.

These observations lead us to the provisional working hypothesis that the bulk of the high-velocity gas was originally concentrated in clouds of small dimension and presumably small-velocity dispersion, in which state they could have existed for a considerable time. They should then have acquired their present large internal motions only during the last five million years or so, presumably as a consequence of their collisions with the interstellar medium; they gradually expand while being slowed down by further sweeping up gas from this medium. If they are now situated at distances of the order of 1 kpc—as indicated by the data of Münch and Zirin—the interstellar medium must already have considerable density at such large distances from the galactic plane. This, again, leads to the suggestion that the Galaxy would have a substantial gaseous halo.

Of various possibilities to explain the high-velocity phenomena, the following three seem to be at present the most plausible:

1. They are caused by supernova explosions somewhere outside the galactic layer.

2. They are due to material ejected somewhere far away, from the galactic disk, by a superexplosion. The debris would fall back into the disk over a large ring around the point of ejection. In order to produce the quantity of high-velocity gas observed near the Sun, the superexplosion would have had to involve a mass of the order of a million times that of the Sun. The travel times to the Sun would have been of the order of a hundred million years.

3. The clouds are falling into the Galactic System from outside. This would mean that the formation of the Galaxy has not taken place all at once, but is a long-drawn-out process, continuing still at the present time.

All of the three hypotheses have met with serious objections. At the moment the objections appear least formidable for the third case. I must point out, however, that I can hardly imagine a more inopportune time to make a choice, because observations which may furnish a direct test are just about to be made. It is probable that they will radically change our present ideas.

I will not consider all the possible theories on the origin of the high-velocity clouds. For the present I shall confine my discussion to the case where they are assumed to come from intergalactic space. I shall suppose that they are falling into the Galactic System from distances between half a million and a million pc. I shall further assume that they originally moved with random velocities of the order of 50 km per sec, and that the Galactic System has likewise a velocity of this order. In a rough approximation the clouds would then describe hyperbolic orbits around the center of our Galaxy. In the vicinity of the Sun the clouds approaching the center would preponderate over those going in the opposite direction, because all the latter would have crossed the galactic plane in an earlier part of their orbit. For about 60 per cent, this crossing would have taken place within the limits of the Galaxy and would have stopped them effectively. Qualitatively this would account for the fact that we observe more high-velocity gas coming from longitudes opposite the center than from the direction of the center itself. The strong preference for the longitudes between 90° and 180° over those between 180° and 270° is the natural consequence of the fact that we observe from a coordinate system moving with the rotational velocity of the Galaxy, in the direction of 90° longitude.

Though our hypothesis may explain some of the main features of the observed distribution of the high velocities, there can be no doubt that this distribution must be strongly influenced by the inherent large-scale unevenness of the distribution of matter in extragalactic space, as well as by the unknown center of mass motion of our own Galaxy. The pronounced North-South asymmetry in the distribution of the high-velocity clouds would, for instance, have to be attributed to these causes.

We must now consider the total flow of the gas carried by the high-velocity clouds. It is of interest for two reasons. One is that it furnishes information on the intergalactic gas density. The other is connected with the dynamics of the spiral structure in the disk. Judging from the present observations, the flow is so large that it is likely to have considerable influence on the motions in the disk.

From the available observations we can make a fair estimate of the total amount of gas per square centimeter between various velocity limits. In order to estimate the flow, we also have to know the thickness of the layer in which the high-velocity clouds are situated. As a provisional guess we shall take this to be 1 kpc for the clouds with velocities above 70 km per sec. This estimate may well be wrong by a factor of two or three in either direction.

The high-velocity hydrogen must consist partly of gas swept up in the Galactic System. In order to determine the relative amount of the swept-up gas, we must first estimate the original velocity with which the clouds would have entered the Galaxy. If we assume that the only force which has acted on them before this time was the gravitational attraction of the Galactic System, the velocity relative to the galactic center would be about 380 km per sec. If we assume, for lack of better information, that the average direction of the stream relative to the local standard of rest is given by the center of the region where the high-velocity clouds are mainly concentrated, namely 120° longitude and +40° latitude, we find that the original velocity relative to the local standard of rest is about 500 km per sec. Because the present space velocity of the observed high-velocity clouds is about 150 km per sec, we consider that roughly 70 per cent of the gas contained in them would be swept-up galactic gas.

Puppi, Setti, and Woltjer (1966) have suggested that the clouds would have been partly braked by the pressure of galactic cosmic rays. In that case the velocity with which the clouds enter the galactic gas would be lower, perhaps 400 km per sec. But it would still seem probable that something like half the observed high-velocity gas would be galactic.

In order to estimate the intergalactic density we must take account of the fact that near the Galaxy the flow is much larger than at great distances because of the gravitational attraction by the Galaxy. The "accretion" factor involved is about 20, if we consider only the gravitational effect. If there is considerable deceleration by cosmic rays, it will be less by a factor which we may estimate to be between 2 and 3. Taking account of the inflow from the Southern galactic hemisphere, and allowing for the fact that there should presumably be alternating periods in which matter is expelled from the galactic disk instead of flowing into it, we arrive at the following estimates for the original density at distances between 0.5 and 1.0 million parsecs:

Without cosmic-ray braking 14×10^{-29} g/cm^3

With cosmic-ray braking 50×10^{-29} g/cm^3

These values are considerably higher than the "critical" average density in the expanding universe, which is about 1.0×10^{-29}. But in view of the enormous irregularity of the distribution of matter in the universe, and in view of the circumstance that we are part of the local group of galaxies, and probably also of the much larger region of excess density surrounding the Virgo cluster, a higher-than-average density is quite possible. But a density of more than 10×10^{-29} can probably be ruled out on the basis of the negative outcome of attempts to measure the HI emission from intergalactic gas. It appears therefore that we come up against a rather serious difficulty, which can be overcome only by appealing rather strongly to the uncertainties in our estimates.

A special problem presented by the high-velocity clouds is whether they can cool sufficiently fast after the ionization caused by the high impact velocities on the galactic gas. This has been studied in Leiden by Savedoff and others; the studies are still in progress.

We shall next consider the effect of the inflow on the Galactic System. A factor of some importance in this connection is whether or not the hydrogen in our Galaxy is mostly in the atomic state. If we use the smallest figures for the flow from outside, and assume that there is only atomic hydrogen, the gas content of the Galaxy would be doubled in about 6×10^9 years. If the incoming stream carries no angular momentum, the angular momentum per unit mass in the galactic layer would be halved in the same period. This appears rather excessive. Probably, therefore, our estimates of the flow are too high.

Shklovskii has drawn attention to one possible way out of these various difficulties. He proposes that the emission by the hydrogen atoms in the halo would be stimulated through a maser action by Ly-α quanta and the background radiation from the universe. There are, however, some fairly serious objections to this possibility. In particular the clouds found by Münch and Zirin (1961) indicate a roughly normal ratio of HI-line intensity to the absorption lines of sodium and calcium.

Although the origin of the high-velocity gas remains hypothetical, we can be fairly certain that in the general region around the Sun there is a large downward current of gas towards the galactic plane. Because of the sweeping up of galactic gas this current is much larger than was estimated above for the stream coming into the outer boundaries of the Galaxy. It is also larger than the current we observe in the high-velocity clouds alone. For as these clouds sweep up more and more galactic gas, the downward current increases in proportion to the relative amount of swept-up gas. At -30 km per sec the flow will be about five times higher than at -150 km per sec. Such a flow would double the layer situated below the average height at which these moderate-velocity clouds are situated in a time of the order of 10^9 years.

Most of this inflow is probably balanced by outflow in other regions of the disk. But it is clear that an exchange of gas on this scale between different parts of the disk must have a large effect on the dynamics of the gas in the disk. The gas involved in this circulation is probably carried to considerable distances from the galactic plane. It therefore forms a sort of gaseous halo around the galactic disk which may extend to several kiloparsecs from the galactic plane, with an average density of the order of 10^{-3} atom per cm^3. Replenishment of the halo may come from type II supernovae in giant associations, or possibly by superexplosions involving very large masses.

Most of the inferences in the latter half of my paper are clearly hypothetical. Real progress can come only from observations. The most crucial observations would be a search for optical absorption lines due to the high-velocity clouds in stars at large distances from the galactic plane. This is the only way to get direct information on their location in space. Such observations may enable us in a near future to obtain a real insight into these fascinating phenomena.

REFERENCES

Blaauw, A., I. Fejes, A. N. M. Hulsbosch, E. Raimond, and C. R. Tolbert (1967), *Radio Astronomy and the Galactic System*, I.A.U. Symposium No. 31.

Burton, W. B. (1965), *Bull. Astron. Inst. Netherlands*, **18**, 247.

Downes, D., A. Maxwell, and M. L. Meeks (1965), *Nature*, **208**, 1189.

Hulsbosch, A. N. M., and E. Raimond (1966), *Bull. Astron. Inst. Netherlands*, **18**, 413.

Kerr, F. J. (1962), *M. N. R. Astron. Soc.*, **123**, 327.

———— (1964), *The Galaxy and the Magellanic Clouds*, I.A.U. Symposium No. 20.

———— and M. W. Sinclair (1966), *Nature*, **212**, 166.

Lindblad, P. O. (1967), *Bull. Astron. Inst. Netherlands*, **19**, 34.

Münch, G., and H. Zirin (1961), *Ap. J.*, **133**, 11.

Oort, J. H. (1967), *Radio Astronomy and the Galactic System*, I.A.U. Symposium No. 31.

——— (1968), *Instability Phenomena in Galaxies*, I.A.U. Symposium No. 29 (still to appear).

Puppi, G., G. Setti, and L. Woltjer (1966), *Nuovo Cimento*, Ser. X, **45**, 252.

Robinson, B. J., and R. X. McGee (1967), *Determination of Radial Velocities*, I.A.U. Symposium No. 30.

Rougoor, W. (1964), *Bull. Astron. Inst. Netherlands*, **17**, 381.

——— and J. H. Oort (1960), *Proc. Nat. Acad. Sci. Washington, D.C.*, **46**, 1.

Schmidt, M. (1957), *Bull. Astron. Inst. Netherlands*, **13**, 247.

Shane, W. W., and G. P. Bieger-Smith (1965), *Bull. Astron. Inst. Netherlands*, **18**, 263.

Westerhout, G. (1957), *Bull. Astron. Inst. Netherlands*, **13**, 201.

C. C. LIN

Spiral Structure in Galaxies

I FIRST LEARNED OF THE SUBJECT to be discussed at this symposium from two lectures given by Professor Oort at a conference organized by Professor Strömgren at Princeton, New Jersey, in 1961. The subject is the spiral patterns which are observed in almost all the highly flattened galaxies, such as our own. The nature of the crucial issues involved has been very well stated by Professor Oort (1962) in the following manner:

In systems with strong differential rotation, such as is found in all non-barred spirals, spiral features are quite natural. Every structural irregularity is likely to be drawn out into a part of a spiral But *this* is not the phenomenon we must consider. We must consider a spiral structure extending over the whole galaxy, from the nucleus to its outermost part, and consisting of two arms starting from diametrically opposite points. Although this structure is often hopelessly irregular and broken up, the general form of the large-scale phenomenon can be recognized in many nebulae.

We are thus primarily concerned with the possible mechanisms that can account for the existence of a grand design over the whole galactic disk. The individual spiral arms are in general broken and patchy, although there are exceptional galaxies, such as the Whirlpool and NGC 5364, which exhibit extremely regular patterns.

The theory I shall present is based on the concept of density waves of the type first propsed by the late Bertil Lindblad more than a quarter of a century ago. (See Lindblad, 1963, and earlier papers.) Both he and his son and successor, P. O. Lindblad, made extensive investigations of orbits of individual stars to find tendencies to form density waves. P. O. Lindblad (1960, 1962) followed these orbits for a group of 192 stars by using modern computing facilities. In contrast, our theory is a direct treatment of the collective modes by using the usual statistical formulation of the principles of stellar dynamics. (See, e.g., Chandrasekhar, 1942.) The detailed analysis, carried out by Lin and Shu (1964, 1966), not only provides a description of the mechanism for self-sustained density waves but also furnishes some fairly general quantitative relationships for comparison with observations, both general and specific. Since the details of these calculations have been partly published and will be more fully published elsewhere, I shall here only outline the main ideas and results and discuss their significance in relation to observations.*

It should be added that, in advocating a theory of density waves, we are not dismissing the existence of material arms formed by the process of differential rotation. The two types of spiral features are in general expected to co-exist. The behavior of the galactic disk associated with such material concentrations has been studied by Goldreich and Lynden-Bell (1965) for a gaseous sheet, and by Julian and Toomre (1967) for a stellar sheet. These processes are perhaps relevant to the "inter-arm bridges" that are often observed, but they do not provide a mechanism for organizing the spiral arms into a pattern extending over the whole galactic disk.

---

* See Lin (1966) for more details of the mathematical theory. A brief outline of the essential mathematical steps was shown at the symposium with the help of slides to illustrate the nature of the analysis.

Q SSS Hypothesis

The focal point of the theory is the hypothesis that there exists, in a galactic disk, a density wave with a quasi-stationary spiral structure (QSSS hypothesis). On the one hand, the consequences of this hypothesis can be checked against observations; on the other hand, the mechanism for maintaining this density wave can be examined from basic principles.

Under this hypothesis, all the components of the galaxy, including gas and young stars, should form spiral patterns in general conformity to the prevailing gravitational field associated with the density wave. Stars with larger dispersion velocities participate with less density contrast. It is visualized that the density variation at any point would be only a few per cent of the basic local mass density. However, this variation can be shown to be sufficient for the gravitational forces to dominate over the hydromagnetic effects for length scales of the order of the galactic radius. Hydromagnetic forces are presumably not negligible when the structure of an individual spiral arm is considered.

The assumption that the pattern is permanent or quasi-stationary, rather than transitory, is based essentially on the following observational fact. We know that there is a typical spacing for spiral galaxies of a given type as determined by other physical characteristics and as shown by the following table:

$$Sa \rightarrow Sb \rightarrow Sc$$

Nuclear concentration	decreasing
Gas content	increasing
Arm spacing	increasing
Total mass	decreasing

The pattern is not expected to be absolutely permanent for a number of reasons. There might, for example, be a superposition of patterns of different pattern speeds; there might be a perennial evolution of the galaxy because of the mean transfer of angular momentum, mass, and so forth, caused by the spiral gravitational field.

Even without the discussion of the detailed mechanisms, the mere assertion of the existence of a density wave with a spiral structure, propagating around the galactic center, leads to implications which can be checked against observations. Indeed, the theory predicts that (1) a spiral arm marked by a given group of young stars must wind up because of differential rotation, whereas (2) the gas whose concentration marks the pattern must have a systematic radial motion. These conclusions follow essentially kinematical considerations. They must be checked against each other and against observations.

Kinematical Considerations

The behavior of the older stars in a galaxy can be readily observed only in terms of a statistical distribution and therefore does not present any difficulties in a physical picture involving a density wave. A similar remark applies to the gas, but here we already have a more serious point to be reconciled. The material velocity of the gas can be observed by the Doppler effect, and it is necessary to show that the radial motion of the gas required by a density wave, circulating around the galactic center, does not exceed any upper limit that might be imposed by observations. We shall see that this is indeed the case in our own Galaxy.

The arrangement of young stars can also be followed in greater detail. It is possible, at least approximately, to draw "isochronic lines" for young stars of the same age. If the winding process of differential rotation is operative, these arms of young stars should be rapidly wound up in the course of one or two revolutions. However, the "lifetime" of these brilliant young stars of the O and

B types is of the order of 10 million years, and the result of the winding process over such a short period is not impressive.

Consider therefore an observer moving with the angular velocity Ω_p of the spiral pattern. The density pattern of the gas will then be stationary, but the gas particles will be moving at a different speed. Let us denote the gas velocity by $(u_\varpi, V + u_\theta)$

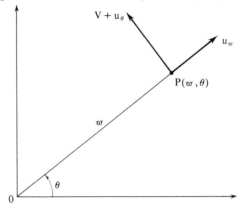

FIGURE 1. Coordinate system in the galactic disk.

(Figure 1). Then it can be shown, by considering the equation of continuity, that the radial motion of the gas has an upper limit u_{max} given by

$$\frac{u_{max}}{V(\varpi)} = \frac{1}{\pi} \frac{\Delta\varpi}{\varpi} \frac{1-r}{1+r} \left(1 - \frac{\Omega_p}{\Omega}\right) \tag{1}$$

where $\Delta\varpi$ is the spacing between two successive arms around the location ϖ, r is the ratio of minimum surface density of the gas to its maximum surface density, and Ω is the angular velocity at ϖ. If we take

$$r = \tfrac{1}{3}, \qquad \Delta\varpi = 2 \text{ kpc} \qquad \text{at} \qquad \varpi = 5 \text{ kpc}$$
$$\Omega = 50 \text{ km/sec-kpc}, \qquad \Omega_p = 20 \text{ km/sec-kpc}$$
$$V = 250 \text{ km/sec}$$

we obtain

$$u_{\max} = 8 \text{ km/sec} \qquad (2)$$

This is safely within the upper limit of 10 km per sec set by observations (van Woerden, Takabubo, and Braes, 1962).

Consider now the behavior of the young stars as seen by an observer moving with the pattern speed. They are presumed to be

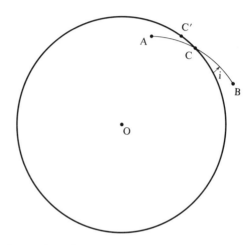

FIGURE 2. Motion of young stars relative to the gaseous arm.

born in the gas concentration ACB (Figure 2). After a time interval Δt, the stars born at C would move ahead of the density wave (which is still at ACB) to the point C' given by

$$C'C = \varpi(\Omega - \Omega_p) \cdot \Delta t$$

The stars born at A would advance further whereas the stars born at B would not advance as much so that the arc $A'C'B'$ would be inclined at a somewhat smaller angle i' ($<i$). But the stars in the arc $A'C'B'$ do not deviate very much from the arc ACB. Indeed, the deviation of C' from ACB is given by

$$\delta\varpi = (\Omega - \Omega_p)(\Delta t) \tan i \qquad (3)$$

If we take the above values of ϖ, Ω, and Ω_p, and $\Delta t = 10 \times 10^6$ yr, $\tan i = 0.11$, we get

$$\delta \varpi = 170 \text{ pc} \qquad (4)$$

Thus the stellar arm is now slightly outside the gaseous arm. There is indeed observational evidence to give general support to this kind of displacement (Zwicky, 1957; Sandage, 1961; Becker, 1964). Detailed comparative study of observational data and theoretical predictions would be desirable.

The change of the angle of inclination is clearly very small over 10 million or even 20 million years. For longer periods of time, the stars merge into the general population and can no longer be distinguished as isochronic lines by age groups. In this way the winding dilemma is avoided as far as the young stellar arms are concerned.

Dynamical Processes

Having passed the "kinematical tests," we now turn to the dynamical basis of these density waves. They represent "co-operative" behavior of the stars due to gravitational interaction aided by a similar behavior of the gas. We shall attempt to demonstrate that density waves of a special structure will be self-sustained at a small but finite amplitude. Suppose such a wave were maintained; then there must be an associated gravitational field of a generally spiral form. We shall start with this field and carry out the analysis as indicated in the diagram shown on page 40.

The resultant gravitational field (0) must be associated, according to Poisson's equation, with a certain distribution of matter (1), which may consist partly of gas and partly of stars. The distribution of gas (2) may be calculated in terms of the resultant gravitational field without any further reference to the distribution

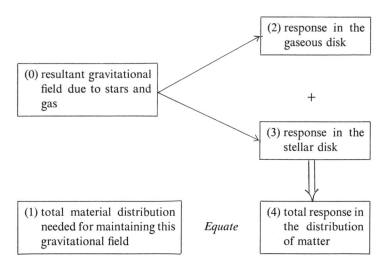

of the stars. Similarly, the distribution of the stars (3) may be calculated without any further reference to the distribution of the gas. The sum of these two distributions yields a total distribution of matter (4) that must be identical with the density distribution (1), which is needed to give rise to the field. This last condition is the equation to be solved for the unspecified functions and parameters that occur in the resultant gravitational field (0) initially assumed.

To describe the spiral waves, we adopt the natural cylindrical coordinate system (ϖ, θ, z) such that the galactic disk is in the plane $z = 0$, with its center at the origin (see Figure 1). In a linear theory, the gravitational potential may be assumed to be given by a superposition of spiral modes, and the response to these individual modes may be treated separately. Let the potential of each of these modes be given by the real part of

$$\mathscr{V}_1(\varpi, \theta, t) = A(\varpi) \exp\{i[\omega t - m\theta + \Phi(\varpi)]\} \qquad (5)$$

where $A(\varpi)$ and $\Phi(\varpi)$ are real functions of the axial distance

ϖ, ω is a complex parameter, and m is a positive integer (or zero in the case of rings). It then follows that all other physical quantities would have a similar distribution. The function $A(\varpi)$ is supposed to be slowly varying with ϖ, whereas the function $\Phi(\varpi)$ is of the form $\varepsilon^{-1}\phi(\varpi)$, where $\phi(\varpi)$ is slowly varying (and monotonic) and ε is a small parameter of the order of the angle of inclination i of the spiral arms. Indeed, the function (equation 5) clearly has a spiral structure described by the family of curves

$$m(\theta - \theta_0) = \Phi(\varpi) - \Phi(\varpi_0) \tag{6}$$

which has m branches and an angle of inclination i given by

$$(k\varpi)^{-1} = \frac{1}{m} \tan i \tag{7}$$

where $k(\varpi) = \Phi'(\varpi)$. We note that

$$\lambda = \frac{2\pi}{|k(\varpi)|} \tag{8}$$

is essentially the wavelength in the radial direction, i.e., the spacing between successive spiral arms. Thus a natural approach is to adopt an asymptotic solution based on a rapidly varying phase angle, with the aid of the small parameter ε mentioned above.

The detailed analysis will be given elsewhere. To the initial approximation, we find (see equation 10 below) that there are neutral waves, but no distinction is made between leading waves ($k > 0$) and trailing waves ($k < 0$). This is indeed expected from general considerations of symmetry. Trailing waves are found to be preferred in the next approximation, which includes terms of the order of

$$\varepsilon = \frac{1}{m} \tan i \tag{9}$$

A small amplification rate of this order is found for trailing waves over an important part of the Galaxy. It is expected that this will lead to neutral waves at amplitudes of the order of $\sqrt{\varepsilon}$, when nonlinear effects are included.

Some Characteristics of the Density Waves

In summarizing some of the important characteristics found for the spiral waves I shall give only a crude outline suitable for general comparison with observations. For further details, see Lin (1966), Lin and Shu (1966), and other pending publications.

(*a*) *Trailing waves are preferred*, as mentioned above.

(*b*) *Waves with pattern speed*

$$\Omega_p = \frac{\omega}{m} \tag{10}$$

can be self-sustained only for the range of values of the radial distance ϖ for which the inequality

$$\Omega - \frac{\kappa}{m} < \Omega_p < \Omega + \frac{\kappa}{m} \tag{11}$$

holds.* This range will be called the principal part of the galactic pattern. The implication of this conclusion is that only two-armed spirals can be expected to be prominent in galaxies similar to our own.

To see this, let us refer to Figure 3, which shows, for the 1965 Schmidt model (Schmidt, 1965) of our Galaxy, three curves for $\Omega \pm \kappa/2$ and Ω respectively. There is also a curve for κ, the epicyclic frequency. Suppose we now draw a horizontal line intersecting the vertical axis at some value between 10 and 20 km per sec-kpc, and adopt this for the value of Ω_p. By referring to

---

* An analogous condition in an electromagnetic plasma states that only waves with frequency above the plasma frequency can be propagated.

equation 11 and this figure, we see that a spiral pattern can be obtained for this pattern speed over a prominent part of the galaxy. On the other hand, if the curves shown had been those for $\Omega \pm \kappa/m$, with $m \neq 2$, the principal part would be so narrow that a pattern could hardly be said to be present.

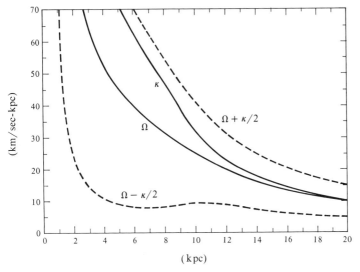

FIGURE 3. Angular velocity, etc., of the 1965 Schmidt model of our Galaxy.

B. Lindblad and P. O. Lindblad emphasized, in their form of the gravitational theory, the importance of gravitational resonance in the inner part of the Galaxy. They emphasized the fact that $\Omega - \kappa/2$ is nearly constant over a considerable portion of the galaxy, so that one can have a pattern in exact resonance, i.e., with

$$\Omega_p = \Omega - \frac{\kappa}{2}, \text{ a constant} \tag{12}$$

The above discussions yield a somewhat different picture. It is necessary for $\Omega - \kappa/2$ to be nearly constant so that the pattern could extend over a wide range of values of the radial distance, but the condition (equation 12) for equality is replaced by equation 11 for inequality. The reason for this difference in conclusion is closely related to the difference in methods used. In our approach, the effect of the cooperative spiral gravitational field of the stars becomes more apparent. We shall refer to the end points of the range (equation 11), where equality holds, as the points of Lindblad resonance.

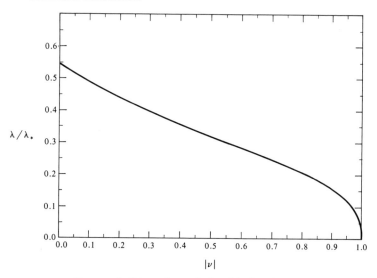

FIGURE 4. Dispersion relationship for density waves.

(c) *The waves satisfy a dispersion relationship such as that exhibited in Figure 4.* In this figure the ordinate is the radial wavelength λ (see equation 8) measured in terms of the length scale

$$\lambda_* = \frac{4\pi^2 G \sigma_*}{\kappa^2} \tag{13}$$

and the abscissa is

$$|\nu| = \frac{|m\,\Omega - \Omega_p|}{\kappa} \tag{14}$$

i.e., the (angular) frequency at which the stars meet with the pattern, measured in terms of the epicyclic frequency κ. In equation 13 $\sigma_*(\varpi)$ is the projected surface density of the stars, and G is the gravitational constant.

This dispersion relationship was calculated by Shu (See Lin and Shu, 1967), using the simplest form of the theory developed on the basis of a disk of stars of infinitesimal thickness, with no gas. The peculiar velocities of the stars are assumed to follow the Schwarzschild distribution with a magnitude barely sufficient to stabilize the disk against gravitational collapse (Toomre, 1964). Shu has also obtained similar results that include the effects of gas and of finite thickness; but the final dispersion relation is only slightly altered. The main change is in the dispersion velocities required for stabilization.

Construction of a Spiral Pattern

Given a galactic model (i.e., if $\sigma_*(\varpi)$ and $\Omega(\varpi)$ are given), we can now use Figure 4 to construct a spiral pattern for each chosen value of Ω_p, by using equation 6 in the form

$$m(\theta - \theta_0) = \int_{\varpi_0}^{\varpi} k(\varpi)\,d\varpi \tag{15}$$

Such a pattern is shown in Figure 5, for the Schmidt Model, by choosing $\Omega_p = 11$ km per sec-kpc. The pattern resembles that obtained for our Galaxy from radio observations.

It should be mentioned that there is as yet no criterion to be used to specify the pattern frequency Ω_p. The value 11 was chosen in order to place the Lindblad resonance point at about 3.75 kpc, where the "3-kpc" arm is located. Since the rotation curve for

C. C. Lin

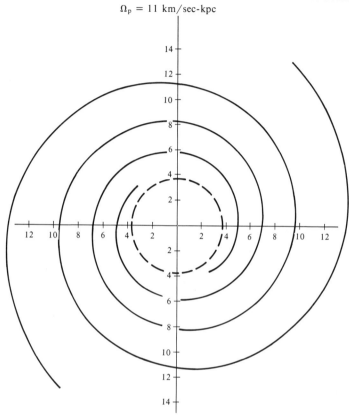

FIGURE 5. A spiral pattern over the Galaxy according to the 1965 Schmidt model.

this point of the Galaxy is uncertain, and the value of $\Omega - \kappa/2$ changes rather rapidly with the radial distance ϖ in this neighborhood, we can regard this choice as only very tentative. Indeed, other arguments might suggest somewhat higher values.

The uncertainty in comparing the present theory with observations is not limited to the choice of Ω_p alone. There is also the uncertainty in the basic model. Specifically, since the solar neighborhood is at the outer part of the Galaxy, the construction of the galactic model does not yield a highly accurate value for the surface mass density.* This surface density is, however, directly proportional to the length scale (equation 13), which in turn determines the spacing between the spiral arms. I shall discuss these points in more detail later.

An Appraisal of the Theory

In making an appraisal of the theory, it should be emphasized that the primary purpose of the theory is to explain the occurrence of a spiral pattern over the whole galactic disk by providing a mechanism for its maintenance. For this primary purpose, the theory has produced the following conclusions, which appear satisfactory from a general point of view:

1. The theory is free from the kinematical difficulty of differential rotation, and it provides predictions on the systematic motion of the gas which can be checked against observations.

2. The theory enables us to provide a mechanism to explain the existence of a spiral pattern over the whole disk while allowing the individual spiral arms to be broken and fragmentary.

3. The theory indicates that two-armed trailing patterns are generally to be expected, in agreement with observations.

4. The scales of the patterns obtained from the theory are in general conformity with those observed, allowing for the uncertainties mentioned above.

There are at least two important implications of the theory of density waves:

1. The first is the systematic motion of the gas implied by the density wave theory. This has a direct bearing on the reduction of data obtained from radio observations. Even without this systematic motion, the radio observations already suffer from a

---

* The value of this mass density is given by Schmidt as $53\,M_\odot/(\text{pc})^2$ in the 1956 model, and as $114\,M_\odot/(\text{pc})^2$ in the 1965 model.

two-valued ambiguity in the assignment of distance (and hence also of gas content). For example, suppose there is a circular spiral arm of gas passing through our neighborhood. The observable motion in the line-of-sight is expected to be very small in any case, and care must be exercised to distinguish it from local features. Such difficulties are obviously greatly increased by the presence of systematic motions.

It would be very interesting to see if a better picture of the structure of the Galaxy can be arrived at from radio observations when we make use of the theory discussed here. In particular, the reconciliation of data obtained from the southern and the northern observations might be attempted in this light.

2. Another important implication of the theory is the following. If the distribution and motion of the gas are indeed stationary in the framework rotating with the angular velocity Ω_p, the magnetic lines of force would eventually also settle into a nearly stationary pattern, with a nearly definite magnitude. The lines of force would then be essentially running along the direction of the spiral arm. This conclusion appears to be in general agreement with observations. It would be interesting to explore a theory of star formation under these conditions. We should be inclined to think that gravitational condensation would tend to occur first along the magnetic lines of force. When sufficient matter density is built up, contraction across a spiral arm would be facilitated. But all these considerations belong to a study of the phenomena on or below the scale of a spiral arm, and is therefore strictly beyond the scope of this paper.

The Solar Vicinity

Since more detailed observational data are available in our vicinity, it would be very useful to see what can be deduced from the theory on the local structure of our Galaxy.

Besides the radio observations, we have data on the spiral arms from optical observations. The work of Strömgren and collaborators on the birthplace of stars up to a few hundred million years of age also gives definite indications of the location of spiral arms in the past, and hence its displacement from the present location. The determination of material density distribution in our vicinity has also been a problem that attracted great interest. Finally, there have been extended investigations of the distribution of peculiar velocities of stars in our vicinity.

All these investigations are related to our dynamical theory of density waves in one way or another. Indeed, our theory can be used as a tool to connect several seemingly unrelated observations just cited. However, it should be borne in mind that our theory is essentially directed toward the problem of the galactic pattern. Thus we might expect more uncertainties to occur in its application to local structure (which could depend on hydromagnetic forces). With this in mind, let us examine the several possibilities in which our theory might be compared with observations.

1. VELOCITY DISPERSION OF STARS Toomre (1964) gave a criterion for the minimum dispersion velocity needed to prevent gravitational collapse. He and Julian (1967) are inclined to believe, however, that the mean square dispersion velocity might exceed this minimum by as large a factor as 1.8. On the other hand, Lin and Shu (1966) are inclined to believe that the value would not significantly exceed the minimum needed. A slight excess would of course be needed to counteract the destabilizing influence of the gas. Since observations show deviations from a Schwarzschild distribution, it is difficult to distinguish between these two opinions without a careful analysis of the observational data. There is a slight possibility that the difference *could* influence the theoretical prediction of arm spacing to some extent.

2. DISPLACEMENT OF GAS CONCENTRATION   The investigations of Strömgren and his collaborators can give us the past location of the gas concentration and hence yield a pattern speed Ω_p. This may or may not agree with the material velocity at the corresponding location. This pattern velocity can be checked against values suggested from the density wave theory, or it might be used in the theory for the determination of arm spacing.

3. DENSITY DISTRIBUTION IN OUR VICINITY   The accurate determination of the projected density distribution is especially important for the theory, since it is directly proportional to the arm spacing. We might even be inclined to turn the problem around and attempt to use the spacing as an aid for the determination of the surface density. Whichever way it might be used, this particular relationship could be useful for constructing models for other galaxies.

4. LOCAL SPIRAL STRUCTURE   Observations on the details of local spiral structure suggest a number of difficulties. The optical data do not stand in good agreement with radio data, which also show differences between northern and southern observations. The latter is of course particularly sensitive to the effect of systematic motions of the gas when the distances from us are small. The Orion arm, as obtained from optical data, seems to show such a large inclination to the circular direction that it might even be an "inter-arm bridge." It would be extremely interesting to attempt to clarify the local structure by reconciling all the observational data with the help of the present theory. Much work remains to be done. In the absence of conclusive observational data, the theoretician can perhaps work out a few alternatives to suggest future observational programs.

NOTE ADDED IN PROOF.   According to our present estimates, the numerical values adopted for arriving at equation 2 are not accurate, but the final result is not substantially changed. See paper to be published by C. C. Lin, C. Yuan, and F. H. Shu, "On the Spiral Structure of Disk Galaxies, III: Comparison with Observations."

The work reported in this paper was supported in part by the National Science Foundation and the National Aeronautics and Space Administration.

REFERENCES

Becker, W. (1964), *Z. Astrophys.*, **58**, 202–10.

Chandrasekhar, S. (1942), *Principles of Stellar Dynamics* (New York: Dover Publications).

Goldreich, P., and D. Lynden-Bell (1965), *M.N.*, **130**, 97–124, 125–58.

Julian, W. H., and A. Toomre (1966), *Ap. J.*, **146**, 810–30.

Lin, C. C. (1966), *J. SIAM Appl. Math.*, **14**, 876–921.

—— and F. H. Shu (1964), *Ap. J.*, **140**, 646–55.

—— and F. H. Shu (1966), *Proc. Nat. Acad. Sci.*, **55**, 229–34.

—— and F. H. Shu (1967), *Proc. IAU-URSI*, Symposium No. 31.

Lindblad, B. (1963), *Stockholm Obs. Ann.*, **22**, 3–20.

Lindblad, P. O. (1960), *Stockholm Obs. Ann.*, **21**, 3–73.

—— (1962), *Interstellar Matter in Galaxies*, edited by L. Woltjer (New York: W. A. Benjamin, Inc.), pp. 222–33.

Oort, J. H. (1962). *Interstellar Matter in Galaxies*, edited by L. Woltjer (New York: W. A. Benjamin, Inc.), pp. 3–22, 234–44.

Sandage, A. (1961), *The Hubble Atlas of Galaxies* (Washington, D.C.: Carnegie Institution of Washington).

Schmidt, M. (1965), *Galactic Structure* (Chicago: The University of Chicago Press), pp. 513–29.

Toomre, A. (1964), *Ap. J.*, **139**, 1217.

Woerden, H. van, K. Takabubo, and L. L. E. Braes (1962), *B.A.N.*, **16**, 321–60, especially the first two figures on page 344.

Zwicky, F. (1957), *Morphological Astronomy* (Berlin: Springer-Verlag), pp. 198–201.

BRUNO ROSSI / Some Recent Results of X-ray Astronomy

X-RAY ASTRONOMY IS NOW little more than four years old. The progress made by this branch of science in this comparatively short period has been quite impressive. Some twenty localized sources are presently known. On some of them highly significant spectral measurements have been carried out, even though the resolution achieved so far has not been sufficient to detect possible emission lines over the continuous background. One of the sources has been positively identified with the Crab Nebula by the remarkable lunar occultation experiment carried out by Friedman's group in the summer of 1964. Another source may be coincident with another supernova remnant (Cas A), and two additional sources may be coincident with two extragalactic objects (M 87 and Cyg A).

Until recently, however, none of the remaining X-ray sources had been even tentatively identified with visible or radio objects. This lack of identification was particularly puzzling in the case of Sco X-1, the strong X-ray source, whose discovery in 1962 marked the beginning of X-ray astronomy. Through the observations of three different groups, the location of this source was known with an uncertainty which, according to the more optimistic estimates, was only one fourth of a square degree while, according to the more conservative estimates, was about one square degree. The brightest star within the larger area of uncertainty had magnitude 9. And yet, at wavelengths smaller than 10 Å, Sco X-1 shone with an intensity only ten times smaller than the quiet sun. Obviously an object of such great brightness in the X-ray region, and so unconspicuous in the visible, was nothing even remotely resembling an ordinary star.

At first it was suggested that Sco X-1 might be one of the hypothetical neutron stars that were fashionable some two or three years ago. Subsequent measurements, however, showed that the X-ray spectrum of Sco X-1 did not resemble at all the Planck spectrum characteristic of a hot, optically thick object. In fact the spectrum measured by a number of observers could be best fitted to an exponential law, such as was expected if the source was a hot, optically thin cloud of fully ionized gas, radiating via bremsstrahlung. From the logarithmic slope of the spectrum, the temperature of the cloud was estimated to be of the order of 50 million °K.

To be sure, this was not the only possible interpretation of the observed spectrum. For example, synchrotron radiation by electrons with a suitably chosen energy distribution could also account for it. However, the source did appear to be transparent to its own radiation, and it was thus reasonable to expect that the spectrum, i.e., the emitted power per unit frequency, should keep on increasing with decreasing frequency, or at least should tend to an approximately constant value. It was then possible from the observed X-ray flux to estimate a lower limit for the visible brightness of Sco X-1. Disregarding interstellar absorption (which, as we shall see, is actually quite small in the direction of Sco X-1), this minimum brightness was found to be equivalent to that of a 13th-magnitude star.

At this point, a second possible interpretation was offered for the absence of a conspicuous visible counterpart of Sco X-1. It was suggested that perhaps Sco X-1 might be the remnant of an ancient and relatively nearby supernova, whose core had expanded to an angular size of several arc minutes. The point was that a cloud of this size, with a total light flux equal to that of a 13th-magnitude star, would have a surface brightness below the limit of detectability. The best angular resolution achieved as of the end of 1965 had placed an upper limit of 7 arc min to the angular diameter of Sco X-1. This upper limit was not yet sufficient to rule out the old supernova hypothesis.

Clearly it was of great importance to improve by a substantial amount the accuracy in the determination of both the angular size and the angular coordinates of Sco X-1. This dual aim was achieved by means of a rocket flight that took place in March of 1966. While the prime mover of this experiment was Riccardo Giacconi, a number of scientists belonging to four different organizations have made important contributions. They are:

R. Giacconi, P. Gorenstein, H. Gursky, and J. Waters of American Science and Engineering, Inc.

M. Oda, H. Bradt, G. Garmire, and B. V. Sreekantan of the Massachusetts Institute of Technology.

A. R. Sandage and P. Osmer of the Mount Wilson and Palomar Observatories.

M. Oda, K. Osawa, and J. Jugaku of the Institute of Space and Aeronautical Science and the Tokyo Astronomical Observatory.

The vehicle used was an attitude-controlled rocket. The instrumentation of this rocket represents a qualitative advance over previous techniques of X-ray astronomy. The improvement regards both angular resolution of the X-ray detector and accuracy in the determination of its instantaneous orientation with respect to the stars.

The angular resolution was achieved by means of a modified version of the modulation collimator originally developed by Oda,

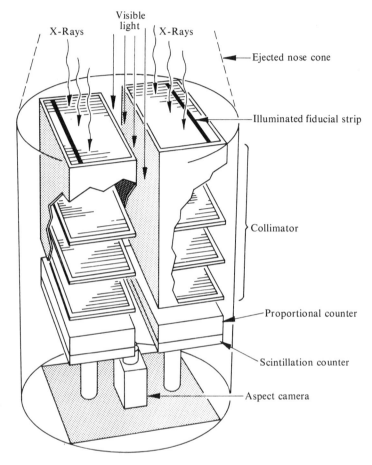

FIGURE 1. Schematic diagram of the collimators and counters used by the ASE-MIT group to determine the angular size and the location of celestial X-ray sources (Gursky et al., 1966a, 1966b).

which combines a wide field of view with a fine resolving power. The rocket contained two separate collimators of this type (see Figures 1, 2). Each collimator was made of a series of parallel

FIGURE 2. Photograph of the collimators represented schematically in Figure 1.

grids; its angular response consisted of a series of transmission bands, about 40″ wide at half maximum, separated by a distance of about 5′ (Figure 3). The radiation was detected by beryllium-window proportional counters sensitive in the spectral region from about 2 to about 20 keV, placed behind the collimators.

The axes of both collimators were parallel to the longitudinal axis of the rocket. The attitude control system caused this axis to point in the general direction of Sco X-1, and then allowed it to drift slowly. Since the collimators have a fine angular resolution only in the direction perpendicular to the wires, the rocket was programmed to roll about its longitudinal axis at some time

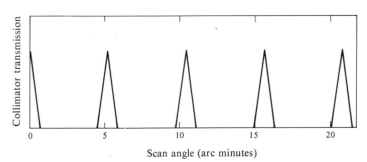

FIGURE 3. Transmission of a modulation collimator as a function of angle in the direction perpendicular to the transmission bands (Gursky et al., 1966a).

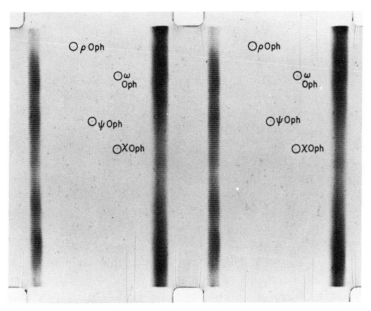

FIGURE 4. Two photographs of star field and transmission bands of the collimators obtained during the rocket flight of the ASE-MIT group (Gursky et al., 1966a).

during the flight, so as to provide angular information in different directions.

The accurate determination of the instantaneous orientation of the collimators' axes was achieved by the inclusion in the payload of a photographic camera, which, during the flight, took pictures of the sky at one-second intervals. To eliminate the possibility of systematic errors that may result from a slight change at take-off in the orientation of the optical axis of the camera relative to the axes of the X-ray collimators, a diffuse light source was arranged in such a way that the star field and the transmission bands of the collimators appeared in the same frame (Figure 4). In this manner it was possible to determine the precise position of the transmission bands at the times when maxima of the transmitted X-ray intensity were observed.

The uncertainty that remains as to which of the transmission bands actually contained the X-ray source was greatly reduced by the use of a "vernier" method, suggested by Gursky and based on a 5 per cent difference in the separation between the transmission bands of the two collimators.

Not much elaboration of the data was needed to obtain the desired information concerning the angular size of Sco X-1. When the counting rates were plotted against time, they showed a series of narrow peaks due to the drift of the X-ray source across the transmission bands of the collimators. An example of such records is shown in Figure 5. In Figure 6 the data corresponding to several peaks are superposed to improve the statistical accuracy, and the resulting experimental variation of the counting rate is compared with that computed for a point source. The agreement is as good as we might expect considering the unavoidable small imperfections of the collimator and the uncertainties in the superposition of the different peaks.

On the basis of this result, the authors announced in April of 1966 that the angular dimensions of Sco X-1 cannot exceed 20″

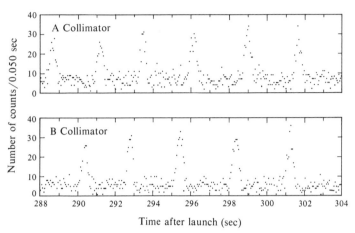

FIGURE 5. Actual counts accumulated during 0.050 sec from each collimator plotted as a function of time after launch. The two collimators differed in their band separation by 5 per cent, which causes a gradual change in phase between the two sets of peaks (Gursky et al., 1966a).

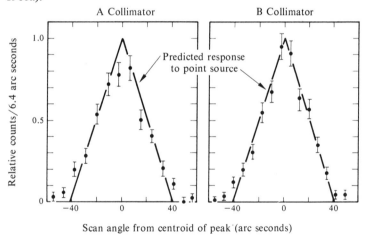

FIGURE 6. Superposition of the data corresponding to several peaks such as those shown in Figure 5.

(Gursky et al., 1966a). This new upper limit—20 times smaller in linear dimensions, 400 times smaller in area than the previous upper limit for the size of Sco X-1—brought to a sharper focus the difficulty of explaining the absence of any conspicuous visible object in the general direction of the strong X-ray source.

As I mentioned before, the luminosity of the source was expected to be equivalent at least to that of a 13th-magnitude star. A 13th-magnitude object of 20″ diameter or less is well above the visibility limit, and yet no nebulosity of the expected brightness could be found in the region of Sco X-1. It was thus concluded that, in all likelihood, the visible counterpart of this X-ray source was a star-like object.

In the direction of Sco X-1 there are about 100 stars of 13th-magnitude or brighter per square degree. Thus, for a positive identification of Sco X-1 with a visible object, it was essential to determine its position within a small fraction of one square degree. The rocket flight that I have described provided the data needed for this determination. However, the task of extracting from the data the exact position of Sco X-1 was much more difficult and time consuming than the task of determining its angular size. The analysis has now been completed (Gursky et al., 1966b). It yields two *a priori* equally probable locations for Sco X-1, defined by the following coordinates:

Right Ascension	*Declination*
$16^{\mathrm{hr}}\,17^{\mathrm{m}}\ \ 7^{\mathrm{s}} \pm 4^{\mathrm{s}}$	$-15°\,30'\,54'' \pm 30''$
$16^{\mathrm{hr}}\,17^{\mathrm{m}}\,19^{\mathrm{s}} \pm 4^{\mathrm{s}}$	$-15°\,35'\,20'' \pm 30''$

The areas of uncertainty corresponding to the two locations are shown by the two rectangles at the center of the inset in Figure 7. This figure also shows two additional rectangles, representing possible, but *a priori* much less likely, locations for the source. The combined area of the two preferred rectangles is only 4 square arc min, or about one thousandth of one square degree. The new locations are 0.5° or more from those reported earlier.

Preliminary results on the location of the Sco X-1 (which turned out to be very close to the final results that I have quoted) were

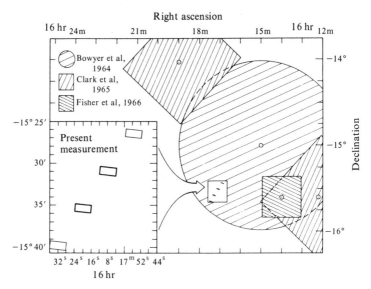

FIGURE 7. The location Sco X-1. The results obtained during the rocket flight discussed here are compared with those from previous experiments (Gursky et al., 1966b).

made available in June 1966 to Oda (who had initially participated in the experiment as the senior member of the M.I.T. group, but had by that time returned to Japan) and, through him, to the staff of the Tokyo Observatory, as well as to A. R. Sandage and his colleagues at the Mount Wilson and Palomar Observatories.

With this new knowledge of the position, a search was undertaken for the visible counterpart of Sco X-1. Again, this was expected to be a star-like object of about 13th-magnitude. Moreover, it should have had an essentially flat spectrum in the visible and ultraviolet regions and therefore should have appeared much more "blue" than ordinary stars.

A two-color image plate (one in the blue, one in the ultraviolet) was taken at the Tokyo Observatory on June 17/18. It revealed the existence of an intense ultraviolet object of visual magnitude 13 near the center of the search area (Sandage et al., 1966). Photoelectric photometry confirmed this result and showed that the spectrum is essentially flat in the visible, so that the object appears much more "blue" than ordinary stars. A spectrogram taken on June 18/19 gave a continuum spectrum, with no absorption features but with faint emission lines. On June 23, photoelectric observations with the 200-inch Palomar reflector confirmed these results. Moreover they showed that the visible light flux from the object varies irregularly by a few per cent in several minutes. A second and improved spectrogram taken at the Tokyo Observatory on June 25/26 showed clearly the emission lines of H and He against a "blue" continuum.

The position of the object was measured at both the Tokyo and the Palomar Observatories. The result was:

$$\text{right ascension:} \quad 16^{hr} \ 17^m \ 4.3^s$$
$$\text{declination:} \quad -15° \ 31' \ 13''$$

A photograph of the sky showing the object in question (arrow) and the two most likely positions for the X-ray source (each surrounded by a rectangle of 2 by 1 arc min, corresponding to the observational uncertainty) appears in Figure 8. The object is about 30″ away from one of the most likely positions. Thus an object of the predicted magnitude and with the predicted color characteristics was indeed found within the very small area of uncertainty for the position of the X-ray source. It was natural to conclude, as the authors did, that this object is the visible counterpart of Sco X-1.

I feel that the chances of a mistaken identification are exceedingly slim. In the first place, while the *a priori* probability of finding a star of 13th magnitude or brighter within an area of

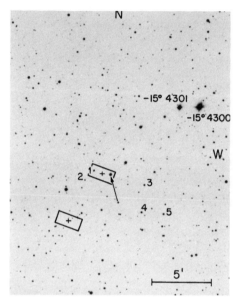

FIGURE 8. Photograph of the region containing the new X-ray position of Sco X-1, reproduced from the Palomar Sky Survey prints. The two equally probable X-ray positions are marked by crosses surrounded by a rectangle of 1 by 2 arc min. The object described in the text is marked with an arrow. The identifications of other stars for which photoelectric photometry exists are also marked (Sandage et al., 1966).

4 square min is 1/10, the probability of finding a "blue" object of this magnitude within the same area is many orders of magnitude smaller. In the second place, no other candidate is available. The next brightest object within the area of uncertainty has magnitude 15, and has the appearance of a normal star. Moreover, a search for "blue" objects conducted at the Tokyo Observatory failed to

detect any within a circle of $\frac{1}{2}$ degree radius around the position of Sco X-1.

In order to determine whether the visible counterpart of Sco X-1 might possibly be obscured by interstellar absorption, observations were made at Palomar of the reddening of several main sequence stars in the immediate neighborhood of Sco X-1. These observations showed that, if Sco X-1 lies anywhere between 100 and 400 parsec, interstellar absorption in the visible amounts to only 0.7 magnitude.

Thus a mistaken identification would require (1) that Sco X-1 is invisible because, against all reasonable expectation, its spectrum decreases with increasing wavelength from the X-ray to the visible region, and (2) that, by an exceedingly unlikely coincidence, an object of the expected magnitude and color characteristics happens to lie within the area of uncertainty for the position of the X-ray source.

Further photometric observations and further spectral measurements were made at the Palomar Observatory in July. The object was found to be highly unstable in its continuum, radiation changing, on one occasion, from 12.6 to 13.2 magnitude in a 2.6-hour period. The emission lines of hydrogen and He II are present, as well as high excitation lines due to C III, N III, and possibly O II. Moreover, the interstellar K-line absorption of Ca II is clearly visible. Large changes were observed both in the actual strength of the Balmer lines and in their strength relative to the continuum.

Searching old plates of the Harvard collection, Garmire and Sreekantan succeeded in tracing the object back to 1896. During the intervening period the object had undergone variations of about one magnitude around a mean value $m = 12.5$, without any indication of a secular trend (Sandage et al., 1966).

An important question is the distance, D, of Sco X-1. The information on this matter is still quite tentative. As far as I know, no measurement of the parallax has been reported as yet. Johnson and Stephenson have looked for proper motion, and found none, within their accuracy of about 2/100 sec per year (1966). From a measurement of the width of Ca II K-line, and under the assumption of a density of 0.5 atom per cm^3, Sandage has estimated the distance to be about 260 pc.

Another important question is that of the angular size. Since it is likely that a sizable fraction of the visible continuum arises from the same process which also produces X-rays, the angular diameter, δ, of the X-ray source should be the same as that of the visible object. Present observations place an upper limit $\delta \lesssim 0.5''$ to this angular diameter.

It is clearly too soon to propose a concrete model for Sco X-1, and I shall not attempt to do so here. I would like, however, to add a few general remarks. The outstanding property of Sco X-1 is obviously its very large X-ray output. This is about 1000 times greater than its energy output in visible light, comparatively much more than for the Crab, or for any other sources for which a tentative identification with a visible object exists. Thus the primary requirement of the model is that it should explain the large X-ray flux.

As I have already noted, the X-ray spectrum suggests bremsstrahlung emission from a hot gas cloud, at a temperature of about $5 \times 10^7\,°K$. It is therefore worthwhile to examine the consequences of this assumption. For the sake of argument, I have assumed that the source lies at a distance $D = 300$ pc, and that it subtends an angle $\delta = 0.5''$. I have also taken the X-ray flux at the earth in the 1 to 10 Å region as $F_{1\text{-}10} = 5 \times 10^{-7}$ erg $cm^{-2}\,sec^{-1}$. Table I lists the assumed parameters as well as some derived parameters, with the indication of how the numerical values of the latter depend on the numerical values of the former.

I would like to call your attention to the rather short cooling time, τ, whose true value is probably considerably smaller than that given in the table, since τ varies as $\delta^{3/2}$. This means that energy must be supplied continuously to the source to maintain its high temperature.

I would like also to note that a cloud of the kind we are considering could be gravitationally contained only if it had at its center a star much more massive than the sun, or if its radius were much

TABLE I *Tentative properties of Sco X-1*

Assumed Parameters

Energy flux 1–10 Å	$F_{1-10} = 5 \times 10^{-7}$ erg cm^{-2} sec^{-1}	
Temperature	$T = 5 \times 10^7$ °K ($kT = 4.3$ keV)	
Distance	$D = 300$ parsec	
Angular diameter	$\delta = 0.5'' = \frac{1}{4} \times 10^{-5}$ rad	

Derived Parameters

Total energy flux	$F = 7.6 \times 10^{-7}$ erg cm^{-2} sec^{-1}	$[F_{1-10}]$
Source power	$P = 8 \times 10^{36}$ erg sec^{-1}	$[F_{1-10}D^2]$
Source radius	$r = 1.1 \times 10^{15}$ cm	$[D\delta]$
Electron density	$n = 0.9 \times 10^7$ cm^{-3}	$[F_{1-10}^{1/2}D^{-1/2}\delta^{-3/2}]$
	$n^2V = 4.6 \times 10^{59}$ cm^{-3}	$[F_{1-10}D^2]$
Source mass	$M = 8.7 \times 10^{28}$ g $\approx 4.4 \times 10^{-5}$ M$_\odot$	$[F_{1-10}^{1/2}D^{5/2}\delta^{3/2}]$
Source thermal energy	$W = 3nkTV = 10.6 \times 10^{44}$ erg	$[F_{1-10}^{1/2}D^{5/2}\delta^{3/2}]$
Cooling time	$\tau = W/P = 13.6 \times 10^7$ sec ≈ 2 yr	$[F_{1-10}^{1/2}D^{1/2}\delta^{3/2}]$
Minimum field for containment	$B = 2.4$ gauss	$[F_{1-10}^{1/4}D^{-1/4}\delta^{-3/4}]$

smaller than the solar radius. The cloud might be magnetically contained, or at least restrained, by a sufficiently strong magnetic field anchored to a massive object at its center. The table indicates that, under the assumptions made, the necessary field strength is of the order of two gauss. Since B varies $\delta^{-3/4}$, this estimate is probably too low.

In the absence of gravitational or magnetic containment, the cloud would expand into space at a speed presumably at least as high as the thermal speed of the protons. We would have to assume that, through a suitable mechanism, the cloud is kept at a temperature of the order of 5×10^7 °K up to a certain distance, beyond which it would cool off by adiabatic expansion. With a density of about 10^7, a radius for the hot cloud of about 10^{15} cm, and an expansion velocity of 10^8 cm sec^{-1}, the mass loss would amount to 4.0×10^{22} g sec^{-1}, or about 6×10^{-4} solar masses ($M_\odot$) per year. The energy loss would be about 2×10^{37} erg sec^{-1}, or more than twenty times greater than the energy output by radiation.

Although the spectrum suggests bremsstrahlung from a hot cloud, it does not rule out other possible mechanisms, in particular synchrotron radiation. In fact it has been shown by Manley (1966) that electrons with a rather flat energy distribution that cuts off sharply above some critical energy E_m would indeed produce a synchrotron spectrum approaching an exponential shape. For the observed spectrum, the critical energy E_m is related to the magnetic field B by the equation

$$BE_m^2 = 0.75 \times 10^{23} \text{ gauss (eV)}^2 \tag{1}$$

The rate of energy loss of electrons of energy E by synchrotron radiation is given by equation

$$-\frac{dE}{dt} = 4 \times 10^{-15} E^2 B^2 \text{ eV sec}^{-1} \tag{2}$$

If we assume that the number of electrons with energy between E and $E + dE$ is given by $N\, dE/E_m$ for $E < E_m$ and is zero for $E > E_m$, then the total power output of the source per cm^3 has the expression:

$$\frac{P}{V} = 4 \times 10^{-15} \frac{NB^2}{E_m} \int_0^{E_m} E^2\, dE$$

or

$$\frac{P}{V} = \frac{4}{3} \times 10^{-15} NB^2 E_m^2 \tag{3}$$

Without attempting to specify the model in more detail, I wish to note that, if the magnetic field is sufficiently weak to allow the free escape of the electrons, the "lifetime" of the source is

$$\tau \approx \frac{r}{c} = 3 \times 10^4 \text{ sec } [D\delta] \qquad (4)$$

On the other hand, magnetic containment of the electrons requires a magnetic field with an energy density at least equal to that of the electrons, i.e., such that

$$\frac{1}{2\mu_0} B^2 = \tfrac{1}{2} N E_m$$

or

$$N E_m = 5 \times 10^{10} B^2 \qquad (5)$$

where E_m is measured in electron volts and B in gauss.

Combining equations 1, 3, and 5, we obtain:

$$\frac{P}{V} = 1.8 \times 10^7 B^{7/2} \text{ eV cm}^{-3} \qquad (6)$$

With $P = 8 \times 10^{36}$ erg per sec $= 5 \times 10^{48}$ eV per sec and $V = \tfrac{4}{3}\pi r^3 = 5.6 \times 10^{45}$ cm^3 we obtain

$$B = 6 \times 10^{-2} \text{ gauss} \qquad [F^{2/7} D^{-2/7} \delta^{-6/7}]$$

$$E_m \approx 10^{12} \text{ eV}$$

In this case the "lifetime" of the source is of the order of:

$$\tau \approx [E/(-dE/dt]_{E=E_m}$$

or

$$\tau \approx 6 \times 10^4 \text{ sec} \qquad (7)$$

In both cases, therefore, the lifetime is of the order of hours (or less, if $\delta < 0.5''$).

In addition to X-rays and the visible continuum, which may have the same origin, the spectrum of Sco X-1 contains various emission lines, whose study is an important source of information concerning the nature of the object. If we assume that the X-ray source is a hot plasma cloud, the first question that arises is whether the same cloud might possibly be also the source of the observed spectral lines, the mechanism being capture of an electron into an excited state, followed by a transition to a lower state. Let us consider, for example, the H_β line.

An approximate computation shows that the equivalent width of the line resulting from the process described above is about 0.4 Å. On the other hand, at the maximum of its luminosity, H_β has an equivalent width of about 6 Å. Thus it would seem that the H_β emission from the hot cloud is more than an order of magnitude smaller that it is observed, at least at the times when the line is most brilliant.

There are two additional arguments against the assumption that the hot cloud is the main source of the H_β line. The first is the observation that the strength of the H_β line relative to that of the continuum undergoes large variations. The second is that the width of the H_β line indicates a temperature much lower than 5×10^7 °K.

Thus we are led to the assumption that the source of the hydrogen lines lies in a comparatively cool region. If the X-ray source is a hot cloud, the cold region may be located inside this cloud, or it may surround it. If the X-radiation arises from a synchrotron process, the cool gas responsible for the line spectrum may occupy the same volume as the high-energy electrons responsible for the X-ray emission. In any case, it is certain that the cool gas is immersed in an exceedingly strong flux of ionizing radiation. This is $(2/\delta)^2$ times stronger than the flux observed at the earth, and thus amounts to at least 5×10^5 erg cm^{-2} sec^{-1}. Thus unless the cool gas has a very high density, it must be almost 100 per cent ionized. This means that the origin of the line spectrum must be fluorescence induced by the X-ray flux rather than collisional excitation. If this is so, the power emitted, for example, in the H_β line has the expression

$$P_{H_\beta} = (n^2 V)_{\text{cool}} \alpha_{42}(h\nu)_{H_\beta}$$

where α_{42} is the effective capture coefficient leading to the H_β emission. An approximate computation, based on the assumption that the temperature of the cool region is 5×10^4 °K, shows that, in order to account for the intensity of the H_β line (when its equivalent width is 6 Å), the ratio $(n^2V)_{cool}$ to $(n^2V)_{hot}$ must have a value of the order of

$$\frac{(n^2V)_{cool}}{(n^2V)_{hot}} \approx 6 \times 10^{-4}$$

We may, for example, make a model, admittedly unrealistic, assuming that the hot cloud is a sphere of radius $r = 10^{15}$ cm, and the cold cloud is a shell of thickness x surrounding this hot cloud. If we assume, moreover, that the two clouds have the same density, we find

$$x = 2 \times 10^{-4}r = 2 \times 10^{11} \text{ cm}$$

The optical depth of such a shell turns out to be smaller than unity at the Lyman edge and greater than unity for the Lyman lines.

Another question is whether a sizable fraction of the visible continuum may originate from the same cool cloud which is the source of the line emission. The ratio between the energy going into the continuum to the energy going into the H_β line must be of the order of the ratio between the total recombination coefficient to α_{42}, a ratio of approximately 10. On the other hand, the energy in the visible continuum is about 500 times that in H_β, when H_β is strongest, and much more at other times. Therefore it seems that the bulk of the continuum must come from the "hot" region.

There are several other pieces of information on this subject. One is the presence of the lines of He II, C III, N III. Can these high-excitation lines come from the region where the Balmer lines of hydrogen originate?

Another piece of information is a recent result of Friedman's group, according to which the energy flux from Sco X-1 in the 44 to

60 Å region is about 10^{-7} erg per cm² sec (Friedman, Byram, and Chubb, 1966). This is about eight times the flux expected on the basis of the observations in the 1 to 10 Å region. Moreover, even if the source were as close as 100 persec, the optical depth of interstellar matter between us and Sco X-1 (computed for $n = 0.5$) would be unity at 44 Å and 3 at 60 Å. Thus the discrepancy between the observed and the predicted value amounts at least to a factor of the order of 50. I feel that it would be very desirable to check Friedman's results, possibly by a more direct method than the two-color photometry used by his group. If these results are confirmed, we would have to accept Friedman's conclusion that Sco X-1 contains, in addition to the "hot" and the "cool" plasma clouds, also an optically thick object (possibly a neutron star) at a temperature of about 2 million °K.

I would like to conclude by mentioning a number of observations potentially capable of shedding light on the nature of Sco X-1.

1. Most important is a search for possible time variations in the X-ray flux, and, if such variations are found, a study of their correlation with the variations in the visible continuum and in the various lines.

2. In order to improve on our present meager knowledge of the distance of Sco X-1, an attempt should be made to measure its parallax. Also, it may be possible to obtain a better estimate of the proper motion than is presently available.

3. It would be most desirable to determine the angular diameter of the visible object, or to reduce the upper limit below the present value 0.5″. Many important properties of Sco X-1 are critically dependent on δ.

4. A search should be made for a possible polarization of the visible continuum; a positive result would, of course, provide evidence for synchrotron emission.

5. I imagine that many additional valuable data will soon be forthcoming from more careful observations of the optical

emission lines and from an extension of these observations into the infrared and ultraviolet. For example, are there forbidden lines? If not, can this be taken as an indication for a high density in the source region? Or can the absence of forbidden lines be explained by the high flux of ionizing radiation in which the source is immersed?

6. If at all possible, we should look for emission lines in the X-ray region. As emphasized by Shklovskii at the recent Symposium in Noordwijk, particularly significant would be the detection of the Fe 24 and Fe 25 lines, which begin to appear prominently only at temperatures of the order of 50 million °K.

7. Finally it is to be hoped that accurate determinations of the positions of other X-ray sources will soon disclose whether other objects similar to Sco X-1 exist. The rate of occurrence of celestial objects with the peculiar properties of Sco X-1 will provide a clue as to whether or not a situation where most of the radiated energy appears in the form of X-rays represents a common phase in the stellar evolution.

The work reported in this paper was supported in part by the National Aeronautics and Space Administration and by the Atomic Energy Commission.

REFERENCES

Friedman, H., E. T. Byram, and T. A. Chubb (1966), *Science*, **153**, 1527.
Gursky, H., R. Giacconi, P. Gorenstein, J. R. Waters, M. Oda, H. Bradt, G. Garmire, and B. V. Sreekantan (1966a), *Ap. J.*, **144**, 1249.
———— (1966b), *Ap. J.*, **146**, 310.
Johnson, H. M., and C. B. Stephenson (1966), *Ap. J.*, **146**, 602.
Manley, O. (1966), *Ap. J.*, **144**, 1253.
Sandage, A. R., P. Osmer, R. Giacconi, P. Gorenstein, H. Gursky, J. Waters, H. Bradt, G. Garmire, B. V. Sreekantan, M. Oda, K. Osawa, and J. Jugaku (1966), *Ap. J.*, **146**, 316.

ALLAN
SANDAGE

The Time Scale for Creation

ONE OF THE INTRIGUING PROBLEMS among current unsolved astronomical puzzles is that of "the age of the universe." It is one of the principal parts of the inquiry into the events of genesis. Both the subject and the problem itself are exceedingly old, and many solutions have been offered, first by the Babylonians and now by the astrophysicists. The methods and the results have changed with time, and, although Bishop Ussher's technique—applied with great energy by scores of authors between the sixteenth and eighteenth centuries—is now somewhat out of fashion, we are perhaps only slightly better off. The "final" answer from astrophysics is not yet in, and the criticisms of the next generation have not begun. Like the Hubble constant, the number for the age of the universe has steadily lengthened as new and better data have become available. Although it appears that the problem is now on its last asymptotic approach toward "certainty," men of all previous ages undoubtedly felt the same.

Even to ask the question about origins requires some audacity and a certain narrowness of view. Cosmologists, long known to possess the necessary boldness, have made this problem their special province, albeit shared by a segment of the eschatologists. It has been argued that the present generation is unique and now has a definitive base from which to work because of three important discoveries made during the past 50 years—discoveries unknown to ancient man. (This position discounts, of course, any future fundamental change which could open new insights, and perhaps even store our present methods along with those of Ussher's in the history of discarded thought; but we ignore this possibility for the remainder of this review.)

The discoveries of radioactivity, the principles of stellar evolution, and the expansion of the universe provide separate handles on the time-scale problem, and current clues persuasively suggest that all three will eventually open the same door. Although the door is cracked a bit, it has not been opened wide, owing primarily to the incomplete state of the present data on distances to globular clusters and to the value of the Hubble and deceleration parameters. In this paper I wish to review the present state of these matters and outline the steps which seem necessary to improve our present data.

General Statement of the Problem

We are beset by a fundamental difficulty at the very start. The time intervals involved are so long compared to laboratory experience that direct knowledge of clock rates over the interval is entirely absent. Since no theoretical connection has yet been made between the microphysics of the atomic nucleus and the large-scale physics of gravitation, there is no *a priori* reason why the time scale measured by a radioactive clock should agree with that measured by the expansion of the universe or by the evolution of the stars. If time has different meanings in the equations of quantum mechanics and of gravitation, a rate between the clocks is possible and the dial readings will diverge as cosmic time progresses. The cosmologies of Milne, Jordon, and Dicke are of this type, and, if such theories are correct, they can be checked by the disagreement of the various experimentally determined time scales, interpreted within some cosmological framework. In this review, we take as a first postulate that no rate in fact exists between the various clocks and we develop therefrom the consequences of a constant ratio theory. If the ancient dates show inconsistencies, then (1) the postulate of zero rate between the various clocks is incorrect, (2) the astrophysical data are suspect, or (3) ancient astronomical history cannot be understood at our present state of knowledge.

Given the event of genesis, any rational cosmology must, almost axiomatically, place the subsequent events roughly in the following order: The time since the creation of the first hydrogen atoms $\geqslant$ the beginning of the expansion of the universe $\geqslant$ condensation of the first galaxies out of the pregalactic medium $\geqslant$ formation of the oldest stars in our Galaxy $\geqslant$ manufacture of the heavy chemical elements $\geqslant$ gravitational contraction of the Sun and the isolation of the solar system from the interstellar medium $\geqslant$ age of the crust of the earth.

One way to test the sequence is to evaluate the time scales for each event and thereby check the inequalities. At the moment this can be done only approximately and for only a few events. Indeed, some of these questions are outside the scientific method. There is a vertical line cutting across the series which divides *science* from *speculation*, and it is a matter of personal taste where this line is to be placed. Conservative workers will put it far to the right, perhaps even between the last and next to the last item. Cosmologists put the line between the first and second items and proceed to discuss the whole of the sequence to the right. We adopt this viewpoint and shall review the evidence for the age of the oldest stars, the age of the chemical elements, and the time since the beginning of the expansion of the world.

The Age of the Oldest Star

The method is so well known that it needs no explanation other than to list the data which must be supplied by the observer and the theoretician.

1. The oldest stars must be located in the Galaxy and persuasive arguments advanced as to why there are no stars older.

2. The distances to these stars must be found so that absolute magnitudes can be determined. Simplifications are possible if the stars are in a cluster because, in principle, the method of photometric parallax may be used. However, for this method to give adequate results, we must have the following information.

3. The color-magnitude diagram must be given well below the main-sequence termination point if the effects of evolution in the photometric fit are to be avoided. If the main sequence is available to less than 4 magnitudes below the break point, theoretical evolutionary tracks must be known to correct for the effects of evolution, as in the method of Johnson (1960), but with a revision for older stars given elsewhere (Sandage, 1962a, Table 9).

4. The interstellar reddening must be known with some precision. In the absence of other uncertainties, an error of ± 0.01 magnitude in $E(B - V)$ produces an error of ± 0.05 magnitude in the distance modulus and in the subsequent absolute luminosity calibration. An uncertainty of this amount produces a 5 per cent error in the age.

5. The age-zero main sequence (AZMS) must be known for the appropriate chemical composition of the cluster in question. This is by far the most difficult part of the problem and is not yet solved. It is known that the AZMS from $M_V = +4$ to $M_V = +8$, defined essentially by the Hyades moving cluster, agrees moderately well with the mean of all trigonometric parallax stars of high weight with $\pi \geqslant 0.''067$ ($r \leqslant 15$ pc. See Figures 2 and 3 of Sandage, 1958a, p. 287). This is, however, a gross approximation on the scale of ± 0.1 magnitude because it is known that stars in the general field cover a wide range of chemical compositions as evidenced by the range of the blanketing indices, $\delta(U - B)$, or Strömgren's m_1 index. This range, if continuous, should produce a continuum of main-sequence lines in the M_{bol}, $\log T_{\mathrm{e}}$ plane,

according to the theory of stellar structure. No cognizance of this is yet made in the method of photometric parallaxes because of (1) uncertainties of the hydrogen (X) and metal (Z) abundance values for individual clusters, and (2) the differences in the $B - V = f(T_e)$ relations as a function of X and Z.

To date it has been assumed that the Hyades sequence is inviolate after blanketing corrections have been applied to field stars and clusters whose photometric parallaxes are desired. Partial justification of the uniqueness of the Hyades sequences has come from a study of the M_V, $B - V$ diagram for parallax stars with differing $\delta(U - B)$ indices after blanketing corrections are applied (see Eggen and Sandage, 1962), but the results are not definitive and are suspect to ±0.2 magnitude because they disagree in detail with the expectations from theory. [Bondi's credibility theorem (1955) is reluctantly applied here.] A fair statement is that to accuracies of ±0.3 magnitude we do not yet have an adequate series of empirical age-zero main sequences for stars of all chemical compositions. Furthermore, we perhaps may have to add a possible systematic error to the distance of the Hyades itself as determined from the moving-cluster method if the suspicions of Hodge and Wallerstein (1966) are correct. Although there has been no general acceptance of this point of view (see Wilson, 1967; Wayman, 1967; Demarque, 1968; Eggen, 1967), the trigonometric parallaxes of high weight with $\pi \geqslant 0\rlap{.}''070$ for stars with $0.8 \geqslant B - V \geqslant 0.4$ would support a correction of about $+0.2$ magnitude to the moving-cluster distance modulus, even though the solution by the moving cluster method is extremely accurate internally (Wayman, Symms, and Blackwell, 1965). The question is by no means settled, however, because Eggen's recent $R - I$ photometry of parallax stars with $\pi > 0\rlap{.}''125$ in the range $1.5 > B - V > 0.8$ shows no such difference with the Hyades.

6. The observed M_V, $B - V$ diagram, presumably now available with correct values of M_V, must be converted into the

bolometric magnitude-effective temperature plane to be compared with theory. Here we need the empirical relations between $B - V$, $\log T_e$, and the bolometric correction. Much progress on this calibration has recently been made for Hyades stars by Oke and Conti (1966) in a study which appears to be definitive in the color range $0.8 \geqslant B - V \geqslant 0.1$, provided, however, that the absolute calibration of the flux via Vega is correct. The temperature scales for stars of chemical compositions which differ from the Hyades can, in principle, be obtained by entering the Hyades $B - V = f(T_e)$ relation with the observed colors after appropriate blanketing corrections are applied following the normal methods (Sandage and Eggen, 1959; Melbourne, 1960; Wildey, Burbidge, Sandage, and Burbidge, 1962). However, these methods have not been completely verified, although the scanner work of Melbourne (1960) and of Strom, Cohen, and Strom (1967) shows that they are correct in first approximation.

Assuming that the observers have done their job correctly, the data on M_{bol}, $\log T_e$ for the oldest stars should now be in the hands of the theoretician, who must construct isochronic lines for stars of different masses and chemical compositions and read the ages of the clusters in question. Following Hoyle (1959), recent work by Demarque and Larson (1964), and by Iben (1967) on the evolution of Population I stars near one solar mass provides an illustration of the method and of the uncertainties. The result is sensitive to chemical composition and to the parameters in the theory of energy transport in the convective envelopes of stars of this mass. These parameters can, in principle, be fixed for the Sun, where the mass, radius, and luminosity are known, and such results give some insight into the case of other Population I stars. The results of Demarque and Larson and of Iben are quite consistent for the case of NGC 188, giving ages in the range of 9 to 12×10^9 years, depending on the chemical composition and on the assumption that the absolute luminosities of NGC 188 stars given by the observer are correct. We note here that recent reobservation of NGC 188 by Eggen and Sandage (unpublished) shows that the original reddening of $E(B - V) = 0.05$ is too small. The correct value is close to 0.10 magnitude. The effect is to make the main-sequence termination point brighter by 0.2 magnitude and the Demarque-Iben ages smaller by 20 per cent.

The outlined six requirements for the observer is a chamber of horrors if, upon entering the problem, we wish to come out the other side with errors less than 30 per cent (0.3 magnitude) in M_{bol}. But enter we must if the prize is to be won, and the remaining part of this section is a recital of the six observational tasks as they are now in the process of being "solved."

The search for the oldest galactic stars is a search for clusters with the faintest main-sequence termination points. The classification system of Trumpler (1925) provided the first clue as to where to look. The method of how to look was provided by the early pioneering results of O. J. Eggen. It can be said that the present era of observational studies of stellar evolution began in the 1950's with Eggen's application of photoelectric techniques to obtain the first modern color-magnitude diagrams of clusters. This was followed by Johnson and Morgan's establishment and exploitation of the *UBV* broad-band system to obtain reddening values and other fundamental calibrations. Progressive study of the $V, B - V$ diagrams for many clusters clearly established the validity of Trumpler's early classification scheme and led by use of Shapley's work (1916), to the isolation of M 67 as a peculiar cluster with a very faint main-sequence termination point. The interpretation of these data followed theories of initial main-sequence evolution established by Öpik, Gamow, Schönberg and Chandrasekhar, and M. Schwarzschild. The result, so obvious today, that the oldest clusters have the faintest termination points for a given chemical composition was not at all obvious as late as 1953, and the recognition of the general evolutionary scheme, primarily by Schwarzschild, Chrandrasekhar, and Strömgren, must be considered the distinguishing feature of this era. McCrea (1962), in his review of the period, emphasized that ours is the first generation that can age-date the stars with qualitative certainty. This must be considered the chief advantage which we possess over the workers in the time of Ussher.

By 1962, NGC 188 had been isolated as the oldest galactic cluster known, with a main-sequence termination point near $M_V = +4.0$. Figure 1 shows the NGC 188 sequence superposed on the M_V, $B - V$ diagram for field stars, as determined by O. C. Wilson (1959) from his method of Ca II emission widths. It is clearly seen that NGC 188 forms the lower envelope of the distribution and that very few field stars exist below this limit, a fact which establishes that NGC 188 must be near the limit of the age of the galactic disk in our neighborhood. However, this in itself is no proof that older stars do not exist, and a different type of argument is necessary.

It is at this juncture that the work of Oort (1926) on the high-velocity stars becomes of fundamental value. The isolation of the Population II stars by Baade (1944) and the identification of this population with Oort's high-velocity substratum of the Galaxy provided the first clue to the early evolutionary history of the Galactic System. The recognition of subdwarfs and RR Lyrae stars as members of this substratum and the connection of these objects with the halo globular clusters opened up the method for identifying the first-generation of stars formed within the Galaxy. The two properties of small density gradient perpendicular to the galactic plane and of high eccentricity for their galactic orbits show that objects of the globular-cluster population differ in a most profound way from stars of the disk Population I.

These facts have been interpreted by various authors, as summarized and extended by Eggen, Lynden-Bell, and Sandage (1962), to appear as the consequence of a collapse of the primeval galaxy

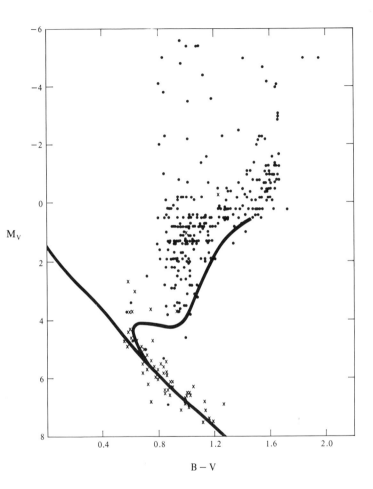

FIGURE 1. The M_V, $B - V$ diagram for the old galactic cluster NGC 188 superposed on the distribution of nearby stars whose absolute magnitudes were determined by O. C. Wilson using his Ca II emission line width method. NGC 188 nearly forms the lower envelope of the distribution. Crosses are trigonometric parallax stars with $\pi \geqslant 0\overset{''}{.}080$.

toward the plane from a more spherical form at an extremely early epoch. Arguments advanced by these authors suggested that the collapse occurred on a time scale close to the free-fall time of about 2×10^8 years and, therefore, that the oldest disk stars cannot be much younger than the oldest halo stars. Identification of the globular clusters as this primeval halo population, based on their great distances from the galactic plane and on the high eccentricity of their galactic orbits (von Hoerner, 1955; Kinman, 1959), predicts that all halo globular clusters should be closely the same age within a spread of only a few times 10^8 years, and furthermore that these objects are the oldest aggregates in the galaxy. The arguments would seem to be persuasive, and item 1 of the observational requirement outlined earlier in this section would seem to have been met.

The next item is then the observation of the V, $B - V$ diagram of globular clusters to determine the absolute luminosity of the main-sequence termination point. This problem, begun in 1952, has continued to the present. Color-magnitude diagrams with differing degrees of precision have been obtained to faint levels for M 92 (Arp, Baum, and Sandage, 1953), M 3 (Sandage, 1953), M 13 (Baum, Hiltner, Johnson, and Sandage, 1959), M 5 (Arp, 1962), and 47 Tuc (Tifft, 1963), and more recently in an unpublished study of M 3, M 13, M 15, and M 92.

Photoelectric techniques with photographic smoothing have generally been used, and a sample of the diagrams now available for M 3 and M 92 are shown in Figures 2 and 3. The data are plotted uncorrected for blanketing and reddening. Significant portions of the main sequence have been observed, but not yet far enough below the main-sequence termination point to be completely free of the effects of initial main-sequence evolution, a fact which must be considered in the photometric parallax determination.

Item 4 of the requirements concerns the value of $E(B - V)$

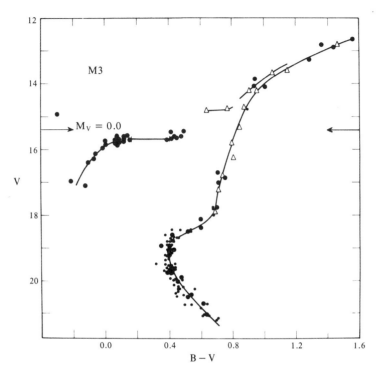

FIGURE 2. The V, $B - V$ diagram for M 3. Large closed dots are photoelectric measurements, small dots are photographically interpolated values averaged from many plates, and triangles are normal points taken from a previous study. The level of $M_V = 0.0$ is shown, determined on the basis of the photometric fit described in the text.

which must be known before a fit to an appropriate age-zero main sequence can be attempted. Small errors in either the reddening or the blanketing, signaled by the $\delta(U - B)$ excess, will introduce large errors in the photometric fit, because the slope of the age-zero main sequence is $dM_V/d(B - V) \simeq 5$ in the region of interest near $M_V = +4$.

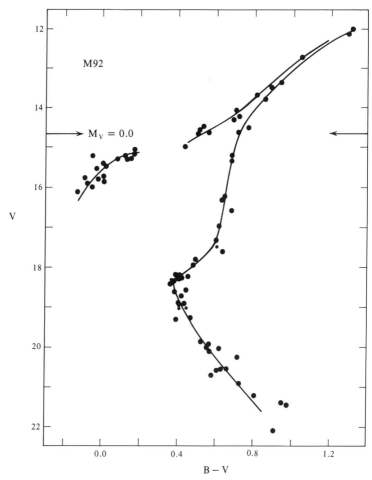

FIGURE 3. The same as Figure 2 for M 92.

We must categorically state that the problem of the reddening is not now solved to within $\delta E(B - V) = \pm 0.05$ magnitude. Various methods, which appear equally valid and precise, differ among themselves by this amount. Three photometric methods, based on certain properties of the *UBV* data for individual stars in and near the clusters M 3, M 13, M 15 and M 92 (Sandage, 1964), agree internally but are substantially smaller (by 0.07 magnitude) than values from two beautiful methods used by van den Bergh (1967) and van den Bergh and Hindman (1967). A similar but smaller difference (0.04) exists with the values based on colors from RR Lyrae variables (Sturch, 1966, 1967). The methods which give the smallest values of $E(B - V)$ are those which use the color properties of (1) the horizontal-branch blue stars, (2) the *F-G* subdwarfs at the main-sequence termination point, and (3) numerous field stars in the direction of the clusters.

Figure 4 shows the new two-color diagram for stars in M 13 brighter than $V = 16.5$. Many horizontal-branch stars are present and are plotted in this diagram. These fit onto the unreddened two-color blue branch for luminosity class V stars. The reasons that we expect unreddened globular-cluster horizontal-branch stars to follow this relation are: (1) The surface gravities of these stars closely imitate the luminosity class V values and (2), even if they differed, Mihalas (1965) has shown that the intrinsic relation is insensitive enough to changes in log g in the range $4.5 > \log g > 3$ so as to cause small or no effect. These data require, then, that $E(B - V) = 0.00$ for M 13. Furthermore, the values obtained from 21 field stars in the direction of the cluster is less than $E(B - V) = 0.02$.

On the other hand, the values obtained for M 13 by van den Bergh and by van den Bergh and Hindman range from 0.03 to 0.11 with a mean of $E(B - V) = 0.08$. The same anomaly exists for M 3 and M 92, where my values are 0.00 and 0.01, respectively, whereas van den Bergh obtains 0.07 for both. The results for M 15 are closer. Van den Bergh obtains $E(B - V) = 0.14$; the result of the present investigation is 0.12. In the diagrams which follow, the smaller 1962 values have been adopted; but we should note that, if the larger values of van den Bergh and Sturch are

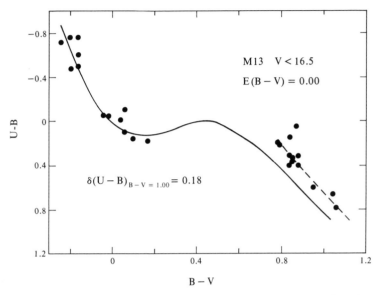

FIGURE 4. The two-color diagram for photoelectric points of M 13. No corrections for reddening have been applied. The normal relation for unreddened main sequence stars is given as the solid line. The agreement of the horizontal branch stars with the unreddened luminosity class V line argues for $E(B - V) = 0.00$. The ultraviolet excess of $\delta(U - V) = 0.18$ of the giants is evident.

adopted, the clusters become more distant, the absolute luminosity of the main-sequence termination point becomes brighter by 0.2 to 0.4 magnitude, the ages are reduced by 20 to 40 per cent, and the absolute luminosities of the RR Lyrae stars become brighter by the same factor. This situation, although unsatisfactory, shows part of the present uncertainty.

We now move to the knotty problem of the appropriate age-zero main sequence to be used for globular clusters. For this first discussion, hampered by the lack of a definitive solution to the problem, we have adopted the empirical results of Eggen and

Sandage (1962), which were that, to within the accuracy of the determination, field subdwarfs with independently known parallaxes and with ultraviolet excess values $\delta(U - B) \geqslant 0.16$ fall on the Hyades main sequence after the blanketing corrections of Wildey et al. (1962) are applied. With this as a basis for modulus fit, measurements of $\delta(U - B)$ for the main-sequence stars of M 3, M 13, M 15, and M 92 were obtained, and appropriate corrections $\Delta(B - V)$ were applied to the observations, which, together with the reddening values $E(B - V)$, generate corrected colors and magnitudes $(B - V)_{0,c}$ and $V_{0,c}$. The clusters were then each fitted to the age-zero main sequence defined by the 16 fundamental calibrating subdwarfs, which themselves were corrected for blanketing. This is equivalent to fitting to the Hyades itself because of the empirical agreement of the two sequences. Figure 5 shows the result for the four program clusters together with 47 Tuc (Tifft, 1963). M 67 and NGC 188 have been added for comparison. The qualitative character of Figure 5 seems well established, even though the absolute placement of the sequences is uncertain by perhaps ±0.4 magnitude, because of the problems involved with (a) the reddening and blanketing values, (b) the detailed failure of the assumption of a Hyades-type age-zero main sequence, and (c) uncertainties in the distance to the Hyades itself. The most striking feature is the near equality of the level of the main-sequence termination points for the five globular clusters. This is a most satisfactory result because it shows with some conviction that all halo globular clusters could be the same age as required in the collapse model of the Galaxy.

The fact that the globular clusters, as a group, turn off at brighter luminosities than the main sequence of NGC 188 does not necessarily mean that they are younger than the oldest disk cluster, because slight changes in the helium abundance can reverse the order of the termination luminosities for clusters of nearly the same age. The effect is well known and follows from the homology

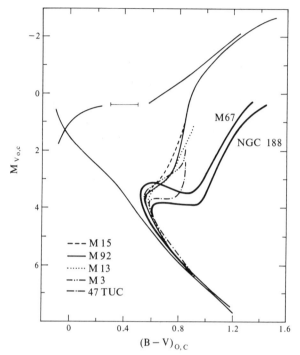

FIGURE 5. The composite diagram of five globular clusters and the two oldest known disk clusters near the main sequence termination point. Corrections for reddening and blanketing have been applied, and a photometric fit has been made to the age-zero main sequence. The upper end of the M 92 sequence is schematic because no adequate blanketing theory exists for giants and subgiants.

approximations, given first by Strömgren (1952), for the equations of the main sequence and the mass-luminosity relation. As a reminder, we note that the age of an aggregate whose main-sequence termination occurs at L_T is given by

$$t = \frac{\text{const } MX}{L_T} \qquad (1)$$

where M is the mass, X the hydrogen abundance by mass, and the constant is determined by the details of the evolving model as to how much core mass is burned into the helium at given L values along the evolving tracks. If we change the chemical composition, but keep L_T constant (imagine two clusters with the same observed L_T but different X, Y, and Z values and ask their age difference), the mass changes and so does t. A rough approximation shows that the mass-luminosity relation is qualitatively of the form

$$M \propto X^{0.8}L^{0.2}Z^{0.2} \tag{2}$$

which, when put into equation 1, gives

$$t \propto X^{1.8}Z^{0.2}L^{-0.8} \tag{3}$$

provided, however, that the constant in equation 1 is not itself a function of X and Z. This shows that the age varies with the hydrogen abundance in such a way that ages can become smaller for increased He abundance, keeping L fixed. This point has also been discussed by Schmidt-Kaler (1961).

However, the true situation is undoubtedly more complicated. Preliminary indications by Faulkner (1967) are that (1) the constant in equation 1 varies with X in such a way as to compensate for the mass effect, and (2) that equation 3 overestimates the effect of chemical composition to such an extent that the ages are more independent of the X, Z values than equation 3 predicts. This comes about because the rise of the evolutionary track above the AZMS for a given core mass is itself a function of X. What the final solution for the age-dating will be depends on how completely the free parameters of the theory can be determined, such as the convective mixing length and the precision to which the energy generation and the internal opacities are known. Uncertainties in these absolute values are such that precise ages are not yet available, even if no errors in the observations or the fitting procedures are admitted. At any rate, Figure 5 is the observational result on the basis of a unique blanketing compensated main-sequence assumption. The individual distance moduli for the clusters were then determined from this fit, and a composite diagram constructed as in Figure 6, where no blanketing corrections have been applied, but only corrections for reddening in $B - V$ and M_V are used. The effect of chemical composition on the slopes of the giant branches is very evident. There is a monotonic progression of the absolute luminosity of the giants at a given $(B - V)_0$ value—say 1.0—from low-metal-abundant clusters (M 15, M 92) to high-metal clusters (NGC 188), in the direction first predicted by Hoyle and Schwarzschild (1955) and later by Demarque and Geisler (1963). The index of metal abundance, $\delta(U - B)$ for the main-sequence dwarfs read at $(B - V)_0 = 0.45$ in the two-color diagram, is listed in parantheses beside each cluster in Figure 6 and indicates the metal abundance of the cluster in question via the calibration of Wallerstein and Carlson (1960).

There are several difficulties in the resulting composite diagram of Figure 6, most serious of which is the near identity of M_V for the RR Lyrae stars in M 15 and in M 3 (not shown). However, the expectation was that the horizontal branch of M 15 should be about 0.3 magnitude higher than that of M 3 so as to explain the mean period difference between variables in these prime examples of the Oosterhoff I and II period groups (Sandage, 1958a, p. 41; Christy, 1966). This requirement seems so strong and it is not met by the present method, that there is doubt about the correctness of some parts of the procedure. Differences in (1) the values of $E(B - V)$, (2) the theory of the blanketing correction, and (3) the assumption of the uniqueness of the Hyades main-sequence fit all play a role. The only independent method of fitting is to assign M_V for RR Lyrae stars via the direct statistical parallax method (van Herk, 1965; Woolley et al., 1965), and let the main sequences fall where they may. This is probably the next approach, but only after a new solution has been made for the M_V calibration, using

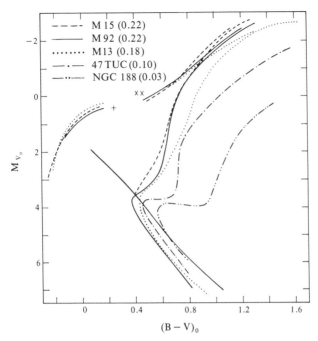

FIGURE 6. Composite diagram for five clusters with only reddening corrections applied. The clusters have been vertically placed by the photometric moduli determined by the method of Figure 5. Difficulties with this procedure are discussed in the text. The two crosses are RR Lyrae stars in M 13. The single vertical cross is a variable in 47 Tuc.

the modern photoelectric data for the field RR Lyrae stars (Fitch, Wisniewski, and Johnson, 1966), and dividing these stars into the two Oosterhoff groups by using the period-amplitude and period-asymmetry relations which are known to differ between M 3 and M 15. It is my belief that we are uncertain in the absolute luminosities of the globular-cluster stars, and in particular the luminosity of the main-sequence turnoff by 0.5 magnitude, using the photometric-fitting procedure. Regardless, then, of the state of the theory, we cannot assign ages more accurately than a factor of about 1.6, which is the uncertainty of the luminosity of the main-sequence termination point. The actual ages assigned to the globular clusters on the basis of the data here presented range from about 16×10^9 years to 12×10^9, according to modern models by Demarque, Faulkner, Iben, and others. A factor of 1.6 on these ages gives a large and comfortable range within which the Hubble constant can be fitted. It is also clear in which direction some of the corrections to the present procedure will carry the problem. If $\Delta E(B - V) = 0.07$ is correct between van den Bergh and the present results, the correction to L_T is $5\Delta E \simeq 0.35$ magnitude, which is, in itself, a factor of 1.4 reduction in any age based on the present data. Adopting 15×10^9 as the age of M 92 (Faulkner and Iben, 1966), obtained by using the present data, would give a corrected value of 10–11×10^9, which is close to the age of NGC 188 as expected from the theory of the collapsing galaxy.

In summary, there can be no doubt that the age of the globular clusters is near 15×10^9 years on any reasonable assumptions concerning the observational data and the theory. However, uncertainties as large as a factor of 1.6 from this value are possible, acting mostly in the direction to decrease the age. In view of this uncertainty, the pessimism expressed recently by some writers on the lack of exact age-scale agreement among the three methods seems entirely unjustified. This becomes even clearer when uncertainties in the ages of the heavy chemical elements and the expansion age of the universe are discussed.

The Age of the Chemical Elements

There have been many reviews of this problem, beginning with the early fundamental estimates of Rutherford. This work was of the highest significance because it changed completely the direction of thought on the time-scale problem in the early years of this century. The age of the elements is here reviewed in some detail as it existed essentially in 1963 and is taken, with some modification, from an unpublished review written in that year. The experts in the field can, with profit, skip this section. The purpose here is to tie together several well-known references as seen from the point of view of an observer.

The very existence of natural radioactive nuclides is highly significant for it proves that the chemical elements are not indefinitely old. Three series of radioactive elements exist naturally; a fourth undoubtedly did exist at an early epoch but has since disappeared because of its short half-life. All natural radioactive elements are daughter products from either Thorium^{232}, which is the parent element of the $4n$ series; Uranium^{238}, parent of the $4n + 2$ series; or Actinium (U^{235}), parent of the $4n + 3$ series. The parent of the $4n + 1$ series is Neptunium^{237}, which has been produced artificially and has a half-life of only 2.25×10^6 years. The half lines and disintegration constants for the parent elements of the three natural radioactive series, determined by absolute counting methods in a sample of known population, are as shown in this table.

Element	Series	Half-life (yr)	λ (yr^{-1})
Th^{232}	$4n$	1.39×10^{10}	4.99×10^{-11}
U^{238}	$4n + 2$	4.51×10^9	1.54×10^{-10}
U^{235}	$4n + 3$	7.07×10^8	9.79×10^{-10}

The difference in the disintegration rates of U^{235} and U^{238} provides a unique radiogenic clock which can give the time since the beginning of first element synthesis, if the past history of the synthesizing events can be found from the evolutionary pattern of the galactic system.

1. SUDDEN SYNTHESIS   The simplest historical model is *sudden synthesis*, where we assume that the three parent elements were formed in a time interval which was short compared with the smallest half-life, and where these elements have been freely decaying ever since. Applying the law of radioactive decay to both U^{235} and U^{238} gives

$$\frac{N^{235}(t)}{N^{235}(t)} = \frac{N^{235}(0)}{N^{238}(0)} e^{-(\lambda_{235}-\lambda_{238})t} \tag{4}$$

where the left side is the present isotopic abundance ratio and the first factor on the right is the abundance ratio at the time of manufacture of these elements.

Laboratory measurements of many samples of the earth's crust give N^{235} (now)/N^{238} (now) $= 0.00723$ with considerable accuracy. The initial abundance ratio $N^{235}(0)/N^{238}(0)$ cannot, of course, be measured but must be derived from some theory of nucleogenesis. The almost universally accepted one of these theories is that of Burbidge, Burbidge, Fowler, and Hoyle (1957, hereinafter called B^2FH). These authors show that the production of the nuclides of high atomic weight must be accomplished by the capture of neutrons by elements heavier than iron. The neutrons are undoubtedly produced in the interior regions of highly evolved stars, and especially in the first stages of supernova explosions. For reasons which we cannot develop here, elements heavier than Bismuth 209 must be made by the capture of neutrons at a very rapid rate, and these conditions are only met in the supernovae. The important point is that the theory predicts the primeval abundance ratio of the uranium isotopes to be $N^{235}(0)/N^{238}(0) = 1.65 \pm 0.03$.

The solution of equation 4 for t then becomes $t = 6.6 \times 10^9$ years as the time interval between our present epoch and that event in the past when the radioactive elements were born. The calculation is not very sensitive to the primeval abundance ratio. If $N^{235}(0)/N^{238}(0)$ had been assumed to be either 1.0 or 2.0 instead of 1.65, then t would have been 6.0×10^9 or 6.9×10^9, respectively.

The same type of calculation can be applied to the Th^{232}/U^{238} ratio, although here the present-day isotopic abundances are not nearly so well known as for U^{235}/U^{238}. Following Suess and Urey (1956), we take Th^{232}/U^{238} (now) to be between 3.0 and 3.5, and, following B^2FH, we take the theoretical primeval ratio to be 1.58, giving t between 6.2×10^9 and 7.7×10^9 years.

2. CONTINUOUS SYNTHESIS We know enough of the early evolutionary history of our Galaxy to suspect that the sudden synthesis model is not correct. For example, data on the chemical composition of Populations I and II stars show that heavy elements have been produced in the Galaxy over a finite time interval since the first stars were formed, i.e., the young stars in the Galaxy are richer in heavy elements than the oldest stars. The age of 6.6×10^9 years from the U^{235}/U^{238} ratio can be increased appreciably if element production occurred over a finite time interval, as follows.

Models of the production history have been computed by B^2FH (1957), by Fowler and Hoyle (1960), by T. P. Kohman (1961), by R. H. Dicke (1962), and by Fowler (1962) on the following basis. Let $t = 0$ be the time from the beginning of element synthesis, and let $t = t_1$ be the time when synthesis was suddenly cut off and free decay of the radioactive elements began; i.e., $t = 0$ is the moment when the first neutron producing supernova explosions began, and t_1 is the moment when the solar system isolated itself from the general interstellar medium by the contraction of the solar nebula during the formation stages of the solar system. This isolation had the effect that additional production of heavy elements in surrounding parts of the Galaxy has not contaminated the abundance ratios observed on the earth.

During the interval from 0 to t_1, let U^{235} and U^{238} be produced at the rates $S_{235}(t)$ and $S_{238}(t)$, which can be functions of time. Under these conditions, the equation for radioactive disintegration is

$$\frac{dN}{dt} = -\lambda t + S(t) \qquad 0 \leqslant t \leqslant t_1 \tag{5}$$

which states that the number of atoms leaving an assembly of a given parent radioactive element per second equals the number of radioactive decays per second, $(-\lambda t)$, plus the number, $S(t)$, added to the assembly by the synthesis per second. Equation 5, as written, holds between the times zero and t_1, whereas equation 5 with $S(t) = 0$ applies after t_1, because we assume all production has stopped. In the particular case where $S(t)$ was constant over the production time, the solution to equation 5 is

$$N(t) = \frac{S}{\lambda} [1 - e^{-\lambda t}] \qquad 0 \leqslant t \leqslant t_1 \tag{6}$$

with the boundary condition $N(0) = 0$.

Equation 6 applied to the uranium abundance ratio at time t_1 gives

$$\frac{N^{235}(t_1)}{N^{238}(t_1)} = \frac{S_{235}\lambda_{238}}{S_{238}\lambda_{235}} \frac{(1 - e^{-\lambda_{235}t_1})}{(1 - e^{-\lambda_{238}t_1})} \tag{7}$$

which can be solved for t_1 if the left side is known, because we take the ratio of the S values to be 1.65 from the nuclear physics involved. The left side can be found if we know how long ago the solar system was formed, i.e., t_1. Fortunately, the age of the solar system is quite well known from the beautiful geochemical dating method of C. Patterson (1956) and others. His data, together with those of J. H. Reynolds (1960), show that the solar system chemically isolated itself from the rest of the galaxy $(4.7 \pm 0.1) \times 10^9$ years ago. The left-hand side of equation 7 can now be found from equation 4, which shows that 4.7×10^9 years ago the isotopic ratio was 0.37, if the present ratio is again taken to be 0.00723.

Substituting 0.37 in the left of equation 7 gives $t_1 = 7.6 \times 10^9$ years, which, when added to the age of the solar system, gives 12.3×10^9 years as the interval between the present epoch and the time when element synthesis first began in our Galaxy. This, then, is the age of the first radioactive elements which were produced, assuming that the galactic production rate of uranium *was constant* in the first 7.6×10^9 years.

3. CONTINUOUS SYNTHESIS AT A VARYING RATE   However, from the data on chemical compositions of the stars as a function of their age, we know that the *assumption of a constant production rate is not correct for our Galaxy*. This evidence is shown in Figure 7, where the ratio of the heavy element abundance to hydrogen is given as a function of age. If the production rate had been constant in the first 7.6×10^9 years, the rise of the curve would be much more gradual than is observed (see Schmidt, 1963). We are forced to conclude that the major phase of element synthesis took place in the early history of the Galaxy, which means that $S(t)$ is a decreasing function of time rather than a constant. R. H. Dicke (1962) and others have considered this problem in detail and, according to the exact model of galactic evolution used, have obtained times for the beginning of element synthesis ranging from 7 to 8×10^9 years ago. In any case, *it is quite certain that this time must be less than the* 12.3×10^9 *years required for a constant production rate.*

To complete the comparison of the age of the elements to the age of the dying stars, we must know the time interval between the birth of the first stars and the beginning of supernova explosions— that is, the time for a star to evolve into the supernova stage. Although the theory of supernovae is not yet complete, it is fairly certain that this time is somewhere between 5×10^8 years if the supernova is a massive star, and perhaps 7×10^9 years if the supernova is of solar mass. Both kinds of supernovae are known

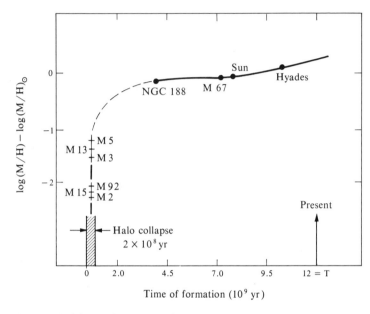

FIGURE 7. Observed change of metal abundance, expressed as the Fe/H ratio to the Sun, with time in the Galaxy on an assumed age of $t_0 = 12 \times 10^9$ years. The rapid increase of the abundance of heavy elements at early epochs argues for an almost sudden synthesis of nuclides heavier than hydrogen during the collapse phase of the galaxy.

to occur, but we do not yet know which kind produces the bulk of the heavy elements. The conclusion is that the time since the formation of the first stars in our Galaxy, determined from this method, ranges from about 8×10^9 years to 15×10^9 years, with the principal uncertainty arising from our inadequate knowledge of the evolutionary time for supernovae.

We may summarize this section as follows:

1. A model of sudden synthesis gives a well-determined lower limit to the age of uranium atoms as 6.6×10^9 years.

2. If synthesis occurred over a *finite* time from the beginning instead of suddenly, and if it proceeded at a rate $S(t)$, then the time since the commencement of element building is greater than 6.6×10^9 years. Estimates of this interval by B²FH, and later by Fowler and Hoyle, range from 6.6 to 12.3×10^9 years, according to the various models of galactic evolution.

3. Dicke, arguing from enrichment data in the galactic disk, suggests that the time over which synthesis occurred is of the order of only 10^9 years. This gives 7.6×10^9 years as the interval from the start of uranium manufacture to the present epoch.

4. If these times are to be compared with the ages of the dying stars, we must add the time of evolution for a star to become a supernova, because heavy elements beyond Bi^{209} cannot be produced until the first supernovae explode. According to the type of supernova required, this gestation time ranges from about 5×10^8 years to perhaps 7×10^9 years. The time of first star formation then becomes 8×10^9 years to 15×10^9 years ago, from these considerations.

The agreement of the age of the chemical elements with the age of the dying stars is one of the most beautiful and unexpected features of astrophysics. Its significance will become even deeper when comparison is made in the next section with the age of the expanding universe.

The Expansion Time Scale

The profoundest of all facts in cosmology is that the universe expands. Current observations of redshifts and apparent magnitudes of the brightest individual galaxies in clusters, spread throughout the range of redshifts of $0.003 \leqslant \Delta\lambda/\lambda_0 \leqslant 0.461$, show beyond all doubt that Hubble's linear law is valid at any given cosmic time with exceedingly high precision. Interim results from an unpublished study of the redshift-apparent magnitude

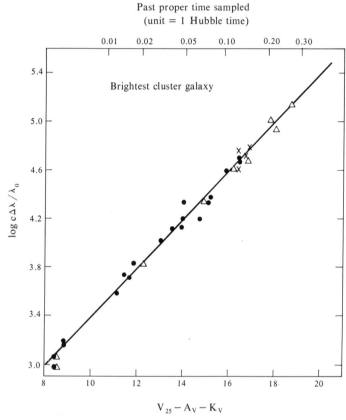

FIGURE 8. The Hubble diagram for the first ranked galaxies in 24 clusters, as available in June, 1966. The nearest points are from the Virgo cluster. The most distant is 3C 295 with a redshift of $\Delta\lambda/\lambda_0 = 0.461$. Solid dots are from the present investigation, crosses are photographically determined points in 1956, and open triangles are from Baum's unpublished data. Plotted is the log of the redshift against the visual magnitude corrected for (1) aperture effect to an isophote of 25 magnitudes per square second of arc, (2) galactic absorption by a cosecant law, and (3) K_V effect of shifting the galaxy spectrum through the V measuring band.

relation for the first-ranked cluster galaxy of 24 clusters of galaxies is shown in Figure 8. The redshifts are from Humason, except for the next to the last two points, where data from Baum (1962), obtained with his photometric technique, are used. The faintest galaxy is 3C 295, where Minkowski's (1960) redshift is adopted.

The line has a slope of 5.0, which is the theoretical asymptotic value as $\Delta\lambda/\lambda_0 \to 0$ for all models, and is the exact solution for the $q_0 = +1$, $\Lambda = 0$ model if no time evolution of the light of E galaxies is admitted. Figure 8 shows that the scatter of the first-ranked cluster members about the line is remarkably small, indicating that the absolute luminosity of the brightest galaxy is a very stable statistic. This important property provides some hope that a deviation of the $[m, z]$ function from linearity can be determined for the eventual evaluation of the deceleration parameter q_0. This parameter, plus the present value of the Hubble "constant," H_0, determines the time, t_0, from the last singularity of the space dilatation factor in all Friedman-type models ($\Lambda = 0$). The well-known relation between H_0, q_0, and t_0 is shown in Figure 9 for radiation-filled universes (solid line) and for matter-filled universes (dotted line) (see Sandage 1961a, Fig. 12).

We are relatively far from the observational solution to this problem. Current estimates of H_0 differ by almost a factor of 2, while q_0 probably lies in the range $2 \geqslant q_0 \geqslant 0$. Besides the difficulty of the observations themselves, a more fundamental problem exists concerning the evolution with time of the light from E galaxies. The time into the evolutionary past to which we look at any given redshift is shown at the top of Figure 8 in terms of the time unit H_0^{-1}. These are derived from equations given elsewhere (Sandage, 1961b) for the case of $q_0 = +1$, $\Lambda = 0$. Assuming $H_0^{-1} = 13 \times 10^9$ years, we look slightly more than 3×10^9 years back into the evolutionary history of 3C 295 with $\Delta\lambda/\lambda_0 = 0.461$. In this interval, the stars in the H-R diagram have changed their main-sequence termination point by about 0.3

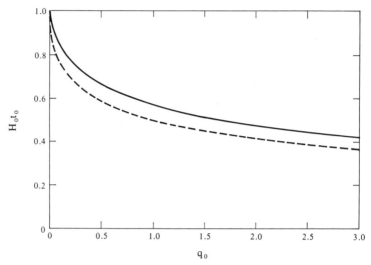

FIGURE 9. The relation between the time t_0 from the last Friedman singularity, the Hubble constant, H_0, and the present value of the deceleration parameter, q_0. The solid line is for a radiation filled universe. The dashed line is for a matter filled universe.

magnitude, and, on simple assumptions of the nature of this diagram and of the luminosity function of E systems, we can, in principle, calculate dL/dt and correct Figure 8 for the evolutionary effect. To do this properly requires knowledge—not yet known with any certainty—of the amount of light tied up in unevolved dwarfs and evolving giants. Work on the integrated spectra and continuous energy distribution of E galaxies, such as that of Morgan (1962), Wood (1966), and Spinrad (1966), is a first step in this problem.

Besides the evolutionary problem, much work remains on the redetermination of H_0 and q_0. We are now in a transition period of the study. Various early estimates of H_0 range from 50 km/sec Mpc (Sandage, 1958b) to 120 km/sec Mpc (van den Bergh, 1968), with intermediate values of 75 (Sandage, 1958b), 98 (Sandage, 1962b), 106 (van den Bergh, 1960), 112 (Holmberg, 1958), and 113 (Sersic, 1960).

A new program now in progress, undertaken with Jerome Kristian, aims at the determination of H_0 using the brightest red supergiants and the angular size of H II regions as distance indicators for Sc and Irr galaxies. Distance moduli as great as 31.0 can be determined, a distance where the redshifts are about 1200 km/sec. The distance indicators are to be calibrated from the primary Cepheid criterion, which itself is calibrated by the nine Cepheids in galactic clusters and associations (S Nor in NGC 6087, DL Cas in NGC 129, U Sgr in M 25, CF Cas in NGC 7790, EV Sct in NGC 6664, and SZ Cas, VX Per, VY Per, and UY Per in the h and χ Per association) via photometric parallaxes through the Hyades. The intrinsic dispersion of the *P-L* relation for Cepheids is now partially understood observationally and can be allowed for in terms of the color width of the Cepheid instability strip in the *H-R* diagram (Sandage, 1958b; Kraft, 1961; Sandage and Tammann, 1968).

The H II regions and brightest red stars can be calibrated in M 33, NGC 6822, LMC, SMC of the local group, and now in all members of the M 81 group (NGC 2403, NGC 2366, IC 2574, Ho I, Ho II, and NGC 4236) because of a new determination of the distance of NGC 2403 (Tamman and Sandage, 1968) based on seventeen Cepheids with periods of 20 to 87 days. The final result for H_0, using some 50 field galaxies with $31 > (m - M)_0 > 27$, is some two years distant, but a formal Hubble constant, based only on the M 81 group at distance modulus 27.56 ± 0.2 and a mean redshift of 201 ± 32 km/sec, is $H_0 = 62$ km/sec Mpc. This single point has little weight because of possible velocity dispersion of the group about the mean cosmological redshift, but it does illustrate that the value of the Hubble constant is not now known within 50 per cent.

The determination of the deceleration parameter is more difficult, and two separate routes are open: (1) Deviations from linearity of the $[m, z]$ relation, properly corrected for evolution of the light of distant E galaxies, can be used. (2) The dependence of the angular diameters of clusters of galaxies on z and q_0 (Hoyle, 1959; Sandage, 1961a, Figure 9) is also available. This latter possibility is now being studied by J. V. Peach and Kristian, using plates taken with the 200- and 48-inch telescopes.

The first method has been pursued in the past, but without current definitive results. Figure 10 is a preliminary diagram which repeats Figure 8 and adds theoretical lines for q_0, but without evolutionary corrections applied. Figure 11 shows new data for radio galaxies (dots) combined with the points of Figure 8 (crosses), again with the lines for q_0 superposed. The formal value for q_0 from these data is $q_0 \simeq +1.6 \pm 0.8$, a value which can be appreciably reduced if dL/dt is strongly negative (Sandage, 1961b; Wielen, 1964). Solutions now in progress by Peach with newer data will soon be available.

There is every hope to improve these data by a large factor in the near future by (1) observing the relevant galaxies in a red pass band near $\lambda \simeq 7000$ Å, when the K_R correction will be small, and (2) increasing the size of sample used in Figure 8 by a factor of about 3 from Abell's catalogue (1958), together with the application of image-tube spectrographic techniques. The calculation of realistic dL/dt values for the evolutionary correction should also be possible once Spinrad's current work on the stellar content of E galaxies is completed. Application of the full theory of the $m(q_0, z, \Lambda)$ relation following McVittie (1965) and Solheim (1966) should then be possible, where Λ can be considered as one of the unknowns in the solution if this is desirable.

A summary of the current data suggests then that $120 > H_0 > 50$, $2 > q_0 > 0$, and $\Lambda = 0$ are possible values. Using these data, we find the extremes for the age to be $19.5 > t_0 > 3.4$ in units of

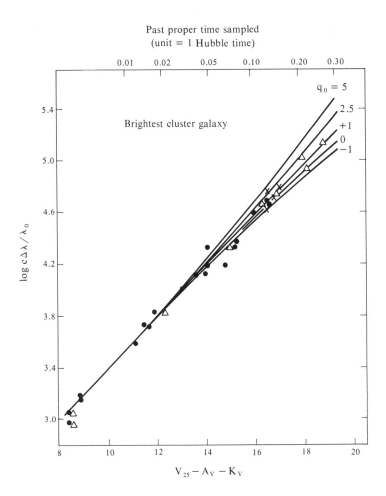

Past proper time sampled
(unit = 1 Hubble time)

FIGURE 10. Same as Figure 8 but with theoretical lines for the deceleration parameter superposed. The evolutionary time into the past history of the galaxies, computed for the model with $q_0 = +1$, $\Lambda = 0$ is shown on top.

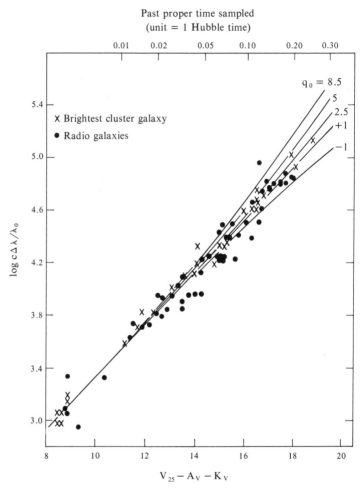

FIGURE 11. Same as Figure 10 for the first ranked cluster members of Figure 8 (crosses), and radio galaxies (dots), identified so far from the 3C catalogue which have redshifts. No normalization of the abscissa has been made, which shows that radio galaxies reach the same luminosity as the brightest E galaxies known.

10^9 years. If we adopt $H_0 = 75$ km/sec Mpc and $q_0 = +0.01$, as suggested from the "observed" density of 2×10^{-31} gm/cm^3 and the cosmological density of $3H_0^2 q_0/4\pi G = 1.5 \times 10^{-29} q_0$ gm/cm^3, then $t_0 \simeq H_0^{-1} = 13 \times 10^9$ years. The obvious great uncertainties preclude detailed discussions of various world models on the basis of the time scale alone. As previously mentioned, it is futile to attempt some of the discussions on the time scale that have recently appeared until these numbers can be appreciably refined. But the one conclusion that can be firmly drawn is that the expansion time scale does agree within its error with the time scale of dying stars and of the chemical elements. This, in itself, is remarkable.

Summary

The deepest motivation of this problem is its connection with the loosely stated problem of genesis. The method of procedure is to test the inequalities stated on page 77 for inconsistencies. Realistic estimates of the errors involved in all three time scales show that no inconsistencies are yet evident. A rational cosmology, starting with a Friedman-type singularity some 10^{10} years ago, followed by a sequence of events through galaxy formation and element synthesis still appears possible. The truly remarkable feature of the present results is not that errors of factors of 2 exist, but rather that the time scales based on such radically different processes agree at all. If no logical connection exists between them, the results could have differed by a factor of a million or more. The fact that they agree so well persuasively points to a time in the past when all astronomical conditions were fundamentally different from the way they are today. There were no heavy elements, no galaxies, no stars. The crossing from that unknown state into the first beginning of our present state with all it subsequent unfolding in time might indeed be called the event of astronomical creation, at least for the world as we know it.

REFERENCES

Abell, G. O. (1958), *Ap. J. Supp. Ser.*, **3**, 211.

Arp, H. C. (1962), *Ap. J.*, **135**, 311.

—— W. A. Baum, and A. R. Sandage (1953), *A. J.*, **58**, 4.

Baade, W. (1944), *Ap. J.*, **100**, 137.

Baum, W. A. (1962), *Problems of Extragalactic Research*, edited by McVittie (New York: Macmillan Company), p. 397, Figure 6.

—— W. A. Hiltner, H. L. Johnson, and A. R. Sandage (1959), *Ap. J.*, **130**, 749.

Bondi, H. (1955), *Vistas in Astronomy*, edited by A. Beer (New York: Pergamon Press), Vol. 1, p. 155.

Burbidge, E. M., G. R. Burbidge, W. A. Fowler, and F. Hoyle (1957), *Rev. Mod. Phys.*, **29**, 547.

Christy, R. F. (1966), *Ap. J.* **144**, 108.

Demarque, P. R. (1968), *Ap. J.*, in press.

—— and J. E. Geisler (1963), *Ap. J.*, **137**, 1102.

—— and R. B. Larson (1964), *Ap. J.*, **140**, 544.

Dicke, R. H. (1962), *Nature*, **194**, 329.

Eggen, O. J., (1967), *Ann. Rev. Astr. and Ap.*, **5**, 125.

—— D. Lynden-Bell, and A. R. Sandage (1962), *Ap. J.*, **136**, 748.

—— and A. R. Sandage (1962), *Ap. J.*, **136**, 735.

Faulkner, J. (1967), *Ap. J.*, **147**, 617.

—— and I. Iben (1966), *Ap. J.*, **144**, 995.

Fitch, W. S., W. Z. Wisniewski, and H. L. Johnson (1966), *Comm. Lun. Plan. Lab.*, University of Arizona, No. 71.

Fowler, W. A. (1962), *Proc. Rutherford Jubilee International Conference* (England, Heywood and Co.)

—— and F. Hoyle (1960), *Ann. Phys.*, **10**, 280.

Hodge, P. W., and G. Wallerstein (1966), *Pub. A.S.P.*, **78**, 411.

Holmberg, E. (1958), *Medd. Lunds. Astr. Obs.*, **II,** No. 136.

Hoyle, F. (1959), *M.N.*, **119**, 124.

—— (1959), *Paris Symposium on Radio Astronomy* (Stanford, Calif.: Stanford University Press), p. 529.

—— and M. Schwarzschild (1955), *Ap. J. Suppl.*, **2,** 1.

Iben, I. (1967), *Ap. J.*, **147**, 624.

Johnson, H. L. (1960), *Lowell Obs. Bull.*, No. 107.

Kinman, T. D. (1959), *Monthly Notices Roy. Astron. Soc.*, **119**, 559.

Kohman, T. P. (1961), *J. Chem. Educ.*, **38**, 73.

Kraft, R. P. (1961), *Ap. J.*, **134**, 616.

McCrea, W. H. (1962), *Quart. J. Roy. Astron. Soc.*, **3**, 63.

McVittie, G. C. (1965), *General Relativity and Cosmology* (Urbana: University of Illinois Press), Chapter 9.

Melbourne, W. G. (1960), *Ap. J.*, **132**, 101.

Mihalas, D. (1965), *Ap. J. Supp. Ser.*, **9**, 321.

Minkowski, R. (1960), *Ap. J.*, **132**, 908.

Morgan, W. W. (1962), *Ap. J.*, **135**, 1.

Oke, J. B., and P. S. Conti (1966), *Ap. J.*, **143**, 134.

Oort, J. H. (1926), *Groningen Pub.*, No. 40.

Patterson, C. (1956), *Geochem. Acta.*, **10**, 230.

Reynolds, J. H. (1960), *Phys. Rev. Letters*, **4**, 8.

Sandage, A. (1953), *A. J.*, **58**, 61.

—— (1958a), *Stellar Populations*, Ricerche Astron, Specola Vaticana, Vol. 5.

—— (1958b), *Ap. J.*, **127**, 513.

—— (1961a), *Ap. J.*, **133**, 355.

—— (1961b), *Ap. J.*, **134**, 916.

—— (1962a), *Ap. J.*, **135**, 349.

—— (1962b), *Problems of Extragalactic Research*, edited by McVittie (New York: Macmillan Company), p. 359.

—— (1964), *Observatory*, **84**, 245.

—— and O. J. Eggen (1959), *Monthly Notices Roy. Astron. Soc.*, **119**, 278.

—— and G. A. Tammann (1968), *Ap. J.*, to be published, February, 1968.

Schmidt, M. (1963), *Ap. J.*, **137**, 758.

Schmidt-Kaler, Th. (1961), *Observatory*, **81**, 226.

Sersic, J. L. (1960), *Z. Astrophys.*, **50**, 168.

Shapley, H. S. (1916), *Contrib. Mt. Wilson Obs.*, No. 117.

Solheim, J. E. (1966), *Monthly Notices Roy. Astron. Soc.*, **133**, 321.

Spinrad, H. (1966), *Pub. A.S.P.*, **78**, 367.

Strom, S. E., J. G. Cohen, and K. M. Strom (1967), *Ap. J.*, **147**, 1038.

Strömgren, B. (1952), *A. J.*, **57**, 65.

Sturch, C. (1966), *Ap. J.*, **143**, 774.

Sturch, C. (1967), *Ap. J.*, **148**, 477.

Suess, H. E., and H. C. Urey (1956), *Rev. Mod. Phys.*, **28**, 53.

Tammann, G. A., and A. R. Sandage (1968), *Ap. J.*, March, 1968.

Tifft, W. G. (1963), *Monthly Notices Roy. Astron. Soc.*, **126**, , 209.

Trumpler, R. J. (1925), *Pub. A.S.P.*, **37**, 307.

van den Bergh, S. (1960), *J. Roy. Astron. Soc. Canada*, **54**, 49.

——— (1967), *A. J.*, **72**, 70.

——— (1968), Chapter in Vol. 9 of *Stars and Stellar Systems*, edited by
Sandage (Chicago: University of Chicago Press).

——— and Hindman, J. V. (1967), preprint.

van Herk, G. (1965), *Bull. Astron. Inst. Netherlands*, **18**, 71.

von Hoerner, S. (1955), *Z. Astrophys.*, **35**, 255.

Wallerstein, G., and M. Carlson (1960), *Ap. J.*, **132**, 276.

Wayman, P. A. (1967), *Pub. A.S.P.*, **79**, 156.

Wayman, P. A., L. S. T. Symms, and K. C. Blackwell (1965), *Roy. Obs.
Bull.*, No. 98.

Wielen, R. (1964), *Z. Astrophys.*, **59**, 129.

Wildey, R. L., E. M. Burbidge, A. R. Sandage, and G. R. Burbidge
(1962), *Ap. J.*, **135**, 94.

Wilson, O. C. (1959), *Ap. J.*, **130**, 496.

——— (1967), *Pub. A.S.P.*, **79**, 46.

Wood, D. B. (1966), *Ap. J.*, **145**, 36.

Woolley, R., G. A. Harding, A. I. Cassells, and J. Saunders (1965),
Roy. Obs. Bull., No. 97, E3.